Douze jours, douze nuits

L'auteur : Marie-Hélène Delval est auteur
de nombreux romans et histoires pour la jeunesse,
publiés aux éditions Bayard Jeunesse, Flammarion…
Pour Bayard, elle est également traductrice
de l'anglais (Les séries L'Épouvanteur
et La cabane magique, *L'Aîné*…).
C'est une passionnée de « littérature de l'Imaginaire »
et – bien sûr – de fantasy !

L'illustrateur : Alban Marilleau a étudié
à l'École Supérieure de l'Image d'Angoulême.
Depuis, il illustre des albums, de la bande dessinée,
et travaille pour Bayard Presse.
Ses ouvrages sont notamment publiés
aux éditions Nathan et Larousse. Pour représenter
l'univers magique des Dragons de Nalsara,
il s'est inspiré des ambiances qu'il fréquentait
déjà enfant, dans les romans de Tolkien.

© 2017, Bayard Éditions
© 2011, Bayard Éditions
Dépôt légal : octobre 2011
Tous droits réservés. Reproduction même partielle interdite.
ISBN : 978-2-7470-3787-7
Deuxième édition - Mars 2019

Imprimé en Espagne par Novoprint
Loi n° 49-956 du 16 juillet 1949 sur les publications à destination de la jeunesse.

Douze jours, douze nuits

Marie-Hélène Delval

Illustrations d'Alban Marilleau

bayard jeunesse

Prologue

À Nalsara,
capitale du royaume d'Ombrune,
dans les derniers jours de l'hiver.

Une aube froide fait scintiller les toitures du palais. La cour de la Dragonnerie royale est blanche de givre. Les dragons s'ébrouent dans leurs box, tandis que les valets leur apportent de l'eau et de la viande fraîche.

Isendrine et Mélisande, les magiciennes, se hâtent dans les corridors : messire Onys, le Maître Dragonnier, les a convoquées dans son bureau.

Il les accueille, le front barré d'un pli soucieux :

— Belles dames, le roi Bertram s'inquiète. Nos voisins du Nord, les Addraks, attendent depuis toujours l'occasion d'envahir Ombrune. Nous savons maintenant qu'ils s'y préparent. Tôt ou tard, ce sera la guerre. Que disent les présages ?

Les magiciennes commentent l'une après l'autre, selon leur curieuse façon de parler :

— Les sorciers addraks ont beau être puissants et se servir de magie noire, ils…

— … sont incapables, pour l'instant, d'engager le combat.

Messire Onys hoche la tête :

— Oui, un chaman, qui habite les grottes de la montagne, a utilisé contre eux une pierre magique.

— Une pierre de Semblance, un…

— … très joli sortilège qui change les êtres vivants en statues !

— C'est cela. Malheureusement, m'avez-vous appris, son effet ne dure pas. À la nouvelle lune, ces douze sorciers retrouveront leur corps de chair.

Cachant d'un même geste leur bouche derrière leur main, les deux magiciennes pouffent :

— Presque ! Ils garderont définitivement…

— … un pied ou une main de pierre !

Messire Onys ne partage pas leur amusement. Les sourcils froncés, il marmonne :

– Ils seront vexés, furieux de s'être laissé ensorceler. Et la colère les rendra d'autant plus redoutables !

Les magiciennes retrouvent leur sérieux :

– C'est certain, messire. Cependant, nous avons maintenant des alliés au cœur des Montagnes du Nord. La tribu du chaman…

– … dont les Addraks ignorent l'existence.

– Oui, le Libre Peuple gouverné par ce Nastrad. C'est une chance que Dhydra et Cham l'aient rencontré. Et nous pouvons compter sur nos dragons.

Le Maître Dragonnier s'approche de la fenêtre, qui donne sur la dragonnerie. Il observe un moment l'activité matinale qui y règne.

« La force militaire d'Ombrune repose sur les dragons, songe-t-il. Les Addraks n'en ont pas, alors que notre armée en possède vingt-sept. Ainsi que vingt-sept dragonniers bien entraînés. Quoique… Ardan et Yénor sont encore très jeunes ; leurs montures aussi. De belles créatures, toutes les deux : Vadir, le dragon d'Ardan, et Nour, celui de Yénor, dont les yeux d'or brillent d'intelligence. Cependant, l'un et l'autre ne sont sortis de l'œuf que l'été dernier… »

À cette pensée, messire Onys se tourne de nouveau vers les magiciennes :

— J'attends des nouvelles d'Antos, notre Grand Éleveur de dragons. Voilà déjà une semaine qu'il est reparti chez lui avec sa famille. Son fils, Cham, devrait revenir au palais dans quelques jours. Dire qu'il va être l'écuyer de Yénor ! Il n'a même pas onze ans !

— Cham est un garçon précieux, commence Isendrine. Il a beaucoup mûri aux côtés de sa mère, quand ils étaient…

— … prisonniers dans la Citadelle Noire des Addraks, termine Mélisande.

— Certes, admet messire Onys. Mais il a encore beaucoup à apprendre. N'oubliez pas qu'il a tenté d'appeler des dragons pour servir les sorciers !

— Il était sous l'emprise de leurs sortilèges. Depuis, il a acquis…

– … de la force et de la prudence.

– Espérons-le! soupire le vieil homme. Si les sorciers addraks avaient, comme nous, des dragons dans leur armée, ils auraient déjà envahi Ombrune…

Le Maître Dragonnier reste un instant silencieux avant de poursuivre:

– Néanmoins, la guerre paraît inévitable. Quant à Cham, bien qu'il montre des talents exceptionnels, il n'est encore qu'un gamin.

– Il est aussi le fils de Dhydra, une grande magicienne, et…

– … le petit-fils d'un puissant sorcier addrak, ne l'oubliez pas!

Isendrine et Mélisande secouent d'un mouvement identique leurs chevelures rouges, qui cascadent jusqu'à leurs pieds:

– Il communique avec les dragons mieux qu'aucun de nos dragonniers, il est…

– … étonnamment doué pour la magie, et peut-être même…

Les deux femmes achèvent d'une seule voix:

– … pour la magie noire!

Ces derniers mots font bondir le Maître Dragonnier :

— Pour la… ? C'est extrêmement dangereux !

Le rire des magiciennes emplit la grande pièce :

— Oh, messire, quand on affronte un serpent, il est bon de savoir…

— … de quoi est fait son venin !

En famille

La vie quotidienne a bien changé, sur l'île aux Dragons. Certes, le travail de la ferme a repris comme avant. Antos soigne les vaches et les brebis, bêche la terre en prévision des prochaines plantations. Cham et Nyne ramassent les œufs au poulailler, nourrissent les volailles et portent leur pâtée aux cochons. Mais Dhydra est là ! Dhydra est revenue, après neuf années où tous la croyaient morte. Elle était, pensait-on, tombée dans la mer du haut de la falaise un jour de tempête. En réalité, enlevée par la strige, elle était emprisonnée dans la Citadelle Noire, sur le Territoire des Addraks.

Depuis leur retour dans l'île, Antos est transformé. Lui qui était auparavant si souvent triste et sévère ne cesse de rire et de chantonner. Ça amuse les enfants. Ils se poussent parfois du coude en gloussant :

— Regarde papa !

— Un vrai amoureux !

Antos attrape à chaque instant sa femme par la taille, caresse ses longs cheveux noirs, lui prend la main pour embrasser le bout de ses doigts. Il a tant souffert de son absence ! Lorsqu'il l'a vue descendre du dos de Nour, dans la cour de la Dragonnerie royale, il a cru étouffer de bonheur.

Nyne, elle, ressent un peu de timidité. Elle n'était qu'un bébé quand sa mère a disparu. Pour elle, cette belle jeune femme, qui est arrivée chez eux il y a une semaine, est presque une inconnue.

Ce matin-là, tandis qu'Antos est à la bergerie et que Cham s'occupe des cochons, Dhydra tend un panier à sa fille :

– Tu viens avec moi sur la colline ? Je voudrais ramasser du petit bois pour le feu.

Elles marchent un moment en silence. Le vent est encore froid, mais un parfum presque printanier flotte dans l'air.

Dhydra déclare enfin :

– Je ne t'ai pas dit combien je suis fière de toi, ma petite Nyne. Tu es venue jusqu'à la Citadelle Noire me rapporter mon miroir. C'était très risqué. Tu t'es montrée très courageuse et très maligne !

Le compliment fait rougir la fillette :

– Sans mon ami Vag, l'élusim, je n'aurais jamais réussi !

– Et moi, sans mon miroir, sans la force magique qu'il m'a donnée, je ne me serais jamais évadée de mon cachot. Si je suis libre aujourd'hui, c'est grâce à toi, ma fille !

Nyne n'a pas encore beaucoup discuté avec sa mère, depuis leurs retrouvailles. D'un coup, elle lâche un flot de questions :

— Maman, la chouette blanche, c'était toi, hein ? Et c'est toi qui as écrit *Le Livre des Secrets* ? C'est toi qui l'as confié pour nous au nicampe, dans le Château Roc ? Depuis quand sais-tu parler aux élusims ? Comment as-tu appris la langue des dragons ? Tu crois que je deviendrai magicienne, comme toi ? Et Cham, il sera dragonnier un jour ? Et la strige, elle…

Dhydra l'interrompt d'un éclat de rire :

— Doucement, Nyne ! Pas tout à la fois ! Le temps viendra où je vous expliquerai bien des mystères, à toi et à ton frère. Je vais tout de même répondre à une de tes questions. Tu devines laquelle ?

Intriguée, Nyne fait signe que non.

Dhydra plonge son regard au fond des yeux de la petite fille :

— Viriana m'a raconté la vision que tu as eue dans l'eau du puits : Cham et moi, avançant dans le tunnel, au cœur de la montagne. C'est un signe qui ne trompe pas. Oui, mon enfant, tu seras magicienne. Tu l'es déjà.

— Oh! lâche Nyne avec un sourire radieux.

Mais sa mère, le visage grave, conclut :

— J'aurais préféré que tu n'hérites pas de mes dons. Car des tâches difficiles t'attendent, j'en ai peur.

Ce soir-là, après le souper, la famille se rassemble devant la cheminée. Antos se tourne vers son fils :

— Sans doute aimerais-tu passer quelques jours de plus ici. Il faut pourtant que tu retournes à Nalsara. Le roi t'a offert de devenir l'écuyer de Yénor ; c'est un grand honneur.

Le garçon hoche la tête. Être écuyer à la Dragonnerie royale! Quand il a entendu la proposition du roi, il a été fou de joie et de fierté. Maintenant, il n'a plus très envie de repartir. Il se sent bien, à la ferme, auprès de sa sœur et de ses parents. Avant, il trouvait souvent le travail quotidien pénible et ennuyeux; il lui paraît à présent facile et reposant. Après tout ce qu'il a vécu! Il a été enlevé par la strige, emprisonné à la Citadelle Noire. Là-bas, il a retrouvé sa mère; il a également appris que Darkat était le demi-frère de Dhydra. Non seulement Cham est le petit-fils d'un Addrak, voilà qu'il est aussi le neveu d'un jeune sorcier! Et Darkat l'a initié à la magie noire... À ce souvenir, le garçon réprime un frisson.

Comme si Dhydra avait suivi ses réflexions, elle déclare:

— Tu as subi de nombreuses épreuves, mon fils. Et tu en es sorti plus fort. Tu as encore beaucoup à apprendre, mais tu deviendras un puissant magicien et, j'en suis sûre, un grand dragonnier. À la dragonnerie, tu feras des progrès rapides. Et les magiciennes te formeront à la magie.

— Justement, glisse Cham. Isendrine et Mélisande… Ces dames ne… Toi, maman, tu en sais autant qu'elles, peut-être même plus. Est-ce que tu ne pourrais pas…

Dhydra baisse la voix :

— Tu ne veux donc plus devenir dragonnier ?

— Oh si ! Mais je…

— Alors, le coupe-t-elle avec fermeté, c'est à Nalsara que tu dois vivre. Il n'y a pas de meilleure école que la Dragonnerie royale. De plus, je te l'ai dit : tous les mots magiques viennent de la langue des dragons. Qui mieux que ton ami Nour te l'enseignerait ?

Le garçon acquiesce en silence. Antos demande :

— Alors, Cham, je prépare un message pour messire Onys ? Tu es prêt à t'en aller ?

— Oui, papa.

— Bien. Dès demain, j'enverrai un alcyon voyageur au palais de Nalsara.

Nyne a écouté cette conversation sans

19

intervenir. Elle est partagée entre deux senti-
ments : le contentement d'avoir bientôt sa
mère pour elle toute seule, et la tristesse d'être
de nouveau séparée de son frère. Puis une
autre idée lui vient, qui la console tout à fait :

« Moi aussi, je suis douée pour la magie.
Et c'est maman qui va m'apprendre ! »

À Nalsara, les magiciennes sont postées
sur la plus haute tour du palais. Elles se tien-
nent debout, le visage tourné vers l'horizon.
Elles observent dans le lointain la ligne
sombre des Montagnes du Nord, que les
Addraks appellent les Mornes Monts :

– Par-delà la montagne, les sorciers attendent. Leurs cœurs continuent…

– … de battre sous l'enveloppe de pierre. Leurs pensées sont plus noires que jamais.

Toutes deux lèvent les yeux. La lune, au début de son deuxième croissant, dessine un mince C lumineux dans le ciel nocturne.

– Plus que douze jours, plus que douze nuits, commente Isendrine. Et…

– … les douze pierres redeviendront chair, conclut Mélisande.

Un coup de vent fait voltiger leurs cheveux rouges. Il apporte une odeur de métal et de sang.

– La guerre, lâchent-elles ensemble. Ça sent la guerre…

L'histoire de Norlande

Ils sont deux ou trois cents, installés sur des tapis de joncs, dans la grande caverne au cœur de la montagne. Des hommes et des femmes de tous âges, des enfants grands et petits. La lumière jaune des lampes à huile fait danser des ombres sur leurs visages. À la nuit tombée, le Libre Peuple s'est réuni à la demande de Nastrad. Ils vont écouter Mandro, le conteur de la tribu.

Une jolie rouquine d'une douzaine d'années chuchote à l'oreille du vieux chaman :

— Qu'est-ce qu'il va nous raconter, grand-père ?

— Tu vas bientôt l'entendre, Igrid !

— Ce soir, tu as invité tout le monde à venir ici. Pourquoi ?

Le vieil homme fixe le vide de son regard aveugle.

— Le passage de Cham et de Dhydra parmi nous a changé bien des choses, explique-t-il. Le Libre Peuple ne pourra sans doute plus rester caché très longtemps.

— Tu crois que… les Addraks vont nous découvrir ?

— En tout cas, ils vont se poser des questions. Après ce qui leur est arrivé dans le marécage…

Igrid dévisage son grand-père avec angoisse :

— Alors, il faudra se battre ?

— Peut-être. Souviens-toi de ce que nous avons promis à Cham et à sa mère : que nous serons leurs alliés si les Addraks attaquent le royaume d'Ombrune. Ils rêvent depuis tellement longtemps de s'en emparer !

La guerre est une chose terrible, Igrid. Mais voilà trois siècles que les sorciers ont envahi notre territoire, trois siècles que les habitants de Norlande sont réduits en esclavage, trois siècles que nous, le Libre Peuple, nous dissimulons au fond de ces grottes. Étrange façon d'être libre, tu ne trouves pas ?

– Au moins, marmonne la jeune fille, on n'est pas aux mains des sorciers…

Nastrad hoche la tête :

– C'est vrai. Et, pour le rester, nous devons agir. Je vois venir une époque nouvelle. Une époque où les sorciers seront chassés, où Norlande retrouvera sa beauté. Une époque où le peuple de Norlande tout entier pourra s'appeler le Libre Peuple.

Il a prononcé cette phrase d'une voix si vibrante qu'Igrid en est impressionnée. Désignant la tribu réunie, elle murmure :

– Et tu as demandé à Mandro de les préparer à cette idée, c'est ça ?

– Tu as tout compris, fillette !

Une rumeur monte alors, car Mandro fait son entrée, escorté de ses deux élèves conteurs, Saddi et Sappi. C'est un petit homme maigre, au visage osseux, aux yeux perçants. Il a orné ses multiples tresses grises de plumes et de perles en os. Il monte sur un rocher recouvert d'une peau d'ours et lance la formule traditionnelle, celle que tous attendent :

— Il y a longtemps, très longtemps de cela…

— Aaaaaaaaaaaah ! soupire son auditoire, ravi.

Chacun s'approche, enthousiaste, pour mieux écouter, tandis que Mandro entame son récit :

— Il y a longtemps, très longtemps de cela, notre peuple vivait libre et heureux sur la terre de Norlande.

À ces mots, un profond silence tombe sur l'assemblée. C'est à peine si on entend crisser le jonc des tapis qui recouvrent le sol.

— Certes, continue le conteur, c'était une vie rude. Norlande est un pays du Nord, où les hivers sont longs et froids, où le soleil perce difficilement les nuages. Mais le sol est riche et, quand on le travaille avec courage, il produit en abondance les légumes et l'orge, le seigle et le blé. En ce temps-là, les ailes des moulins tournaient au vent de la mer avec des cliquetis joyeux pour moudre la farine ; les boulangers cuisaient des pains à la croûte dorée. Les vergers de Norlande croulaient sous les fruits. Les troupeaux de chèvres et de moutons qui paissaient dans les plaines fournissaient un lait riche, une viande parfumée, une laine épaisse dont on tissait de chauds vêtements. Oui, l'existence était rude. Mais le peuple de Norlande, fier, courageux et tenace, était en paix.

Le conteur marque une pause, laissant ses auditeurs rêver à cette époque bénie. Enfin, il reprend :

— Les rois qui se succédaient sur le trône de Norlande régnaient avec justice, et le pays commerçait en toute amitié avec Ombrune, son puissant voisin du sud. À l'ouest, c'était l'océan. Tout au nord ne s'étendaient que des terres glacées, inhabitées, sinon de quelques bêtes sauvages. Au-delà de la fron-

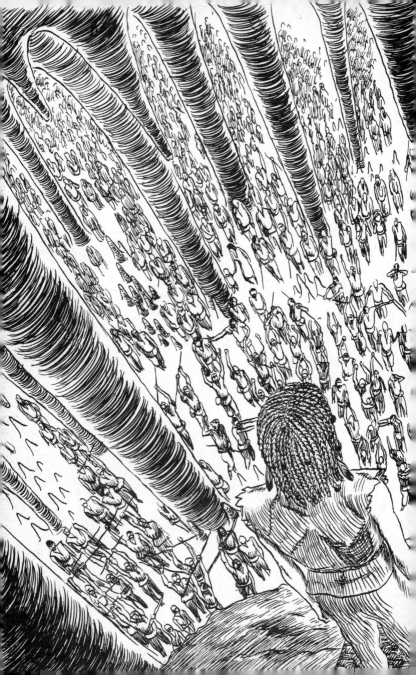

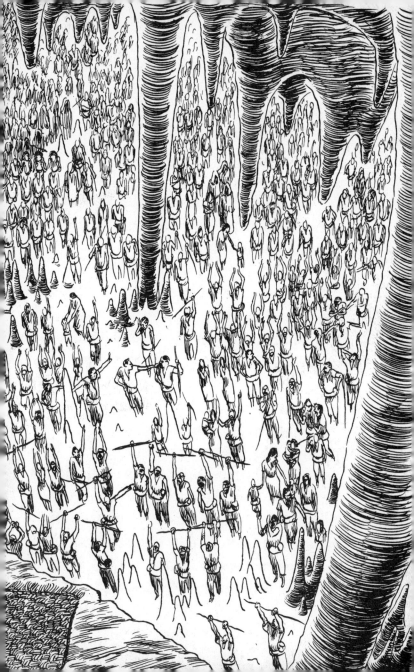

tière de l'est, il n'y avait, croyait-on, que des montagnes désertes et des volcans éteints. Or, voilà trois cents ans, sous le règne du roi Lohr, de mystérieux cavaliers franchirent cette frontière…

Un frisson passe sur l'assemblée. Chacun sait de qui le conteur veut parler. Pourtant, tous attendent qu'il le dise ; pendant quelques instants encore, ils s'autorisent à ne pas y croire.

– Ils n'étaient que douze, continue Mandro de sa voix profonde. Douze hommes habillés de noir, montés sur de puissants chevaux aussi noirs que leurs maîtres. Avec eux, le malheur entrait dans Norlande. Car c'étaient des sorciers. Des Addraks.

De nouveau, Mandro se tait et semble plonger au fond de sa mémoire. Plus personne n'ose bouger. Enfin, le conteur écarte les bras. Ses deux élèves, Saddi et Sappi, lui prennent chacun une main. Tous trois renversent la tête en arrière et psalmodient ensemble, comme s'ils voyaient la scène se dérouler sous leurs yeux :

– Douze hommes noirs, douze sorciers. Partout où ils passent, les cultures sèchent, le bétail meurt, les humains abandonnent leurs maisons et leurs champs. Hommes, femmes, enfants, tous marchent à leur suite, hypnotisés, le regard vide.

Dans la lumière tremblante des lampes à huile, les auditeurs retiennent leur souffle.

Les trois récitants continuent :

– Les sorciers traversent ainsi le pays, répandant partout le malheur et la folie. Enfin ils arrivent devant le palais du roi Lohr. Face à eux, les soldats se figent, pétrifiés. Les portes s'ouvrent toutes seules. Les sorciers pénètrent dans la grande salle où le roi est assis sur son trône, son épouse près de lui. Le souverain se lève pour interpeller les intrus.

Mandro imite alors la voix du roi :

– Qui êtes-vous ? Que cherchez-vous ici ?

Saddi et Sappi enchaînent d'un ton sinistre :

– Pour toute réponse, le plus âgé des sorciers pointe un doigt sur lui.

— Un éclair en jaillit, qui frappe le souverain en plein cœur.

Mandro termine :

— Aussitôt, le roi défaille et retombe mort contre le dossier de bois doré. La reine s'affaisse, inerte, à son côté.

— Ooooooooh ! souffle l'assemblée, atterrée.

Le conteur lâche alors la main de ses élèves. Il se redresse d'un bond sur le rocher qui lui sert d'estrade et, dominant ses auditeurs, il tonne :

— Voilà comment Norlande a cessé d'être Norlande pour devenir le Territoire des Addraks. Depuis, ces sorciers sont morts, mais d'autres les ont remplacés – des fils que ces monstres ont eus avec des femmes de Norlande réduites en esclavage. Car ils doivent toujours être douze. Les blancs chevaux de Norlande ont laissé place à des bêtes noires qu'on croirait sorties de l'enfer. Les soldats de l'armée royale ont été transformés en êtres de ténèbres, armés d'épées noires, caparaçonnés d'armures noires.

Sur l'ordre des sorciers, les hommes de Norlande ont taillé des pierres dans les cratères des volcans pour élever la Citadelle Noire. Ceux qui sont restés pour cultiver la terre ont tiré du sol des légumes et des fruits maléfiques. La magie noire a empoisonné le pays. Et cette malédiction dure depuis trois siècles.

L'assemblée, consternée, garde le silence. Les gens, bien sûr, avaient déjà connaissance de tout cela. Mais ici, dans la sécurité des grottes, au cœur des Mornes Monts, ils préféraient l'oublier.

Une voix s'élève alors, celle de Nastrad :

– Une poignée d'hommes et de femmes, toutefois, ont échappé à l'emprise des Addraks. Ils se sont réfugiés ici, dans le ventre de la montagne. Il y avait un chaman parmi eux. C'est ce qui les a sauvés : grâce à ses sortilèges, les Addraks ne les ont jamais trouvés. Ce chaman était mon ancêtre. Il a transmis ses connaissances à son fils, qui les a transmises au sien. Enfin, elles me sont parvenues. Or, moi, Nastrad, je n'ai pas eu de fils. Mon pouvoir s'éteindra avec moi.

Le vieil homme s'est levé, et son regard aveugle fait le tour de la grotte. S'il ne voit pas les gens, il sent la présence de chacun d'eux.

– Mes amis, reprend-il, nous ne pourrons plus rester cachés très longtemps. Les Addraks savent maintenant que quelque chose se passe ici, à la lisière du marécage, au pied des Mornes Monts.

Un homme l'interrompt d'un ton agressif :

– Ça ne serait pas arrivé si nous n'avions pas abrité ces fuyards, la femme et son fils !

Certains renchérissent :

– Il a raison !

– À cause d'eux, nous voilà en danger !

– On aurait dû les chasser !

– Laisser le marécage les engloutir !

Un brouhaha emplit soudain la grotte, et

les parois de roche se renvoient les échos de cris de colère.

Igrid est devenue toute pâle. Elle tire Nastrad par le pan de son vêtement :

— Fais-les taire, grand-père !

Le vieux chaman lui caresse la tête en souriant :

— Ne crains rien, fillette. Ils vont se calmer.

Au bout de quelques minutes, en effet, l'agitation retombe. Dans le silence revenu, une voix d'enfant s'élève :

— Qu'est-ce qu'on fait, maintenant ?

Instinctivement, tous les yeux se tournent vers Nastrad.

— Ce qu'on fait ? répète celui-ci.

Écartant les bras, il clame :

— On cesse de se terrer dans des grottes telles des bêtes effrayées. On tâche de mériter enfin notre nom de Libre Peuple !

Promesses

Quelque part aux confins de l'océan, l'aube se lève sur le Royaume des Dragons. Là vivent les dragons sauvages. De loin, on croirait voir une île montagneuse, dissimulée dans la brume. En vérité, c'est une gigantesque forteresse de pierre blanche, creusée de grottes profondes, ornée d'arcades et de colonnades, dotée de tours et de tourelles. Du sommet des tours, de vertigineuses flèches de cristal s'élancent vers le ciel. Les premières lueurs du jour y allument des éclats de lumière rose. Le seul humain qui ait contemplé cette splendeur s'appelait messire Damian, et c'est l'ultime vision qu'il a eue avant de mourir. Les dragons ont bâti pour lui un tombeau de diamant où il repose, face à la mer, pour l'éternité. Les dragons passent souvent s'incliner devant celui qui a été le premier des dragonniers.

Selka, une puissante dragonne aux écailles vertes, vient tous les jours, au lever du soleil. Elle s'adresse en esprit à son maître très aimé. L'œuf d'où elle est sortie, il y a bientôt cent ans, avait été déposé dans l'île aux Dragons, qui ne portait pas encore ce nom, et qui était alors inhabitée.

Aujourd'hui, la belle créature est là, comme chaque matin. Et, comme chaque matin, elle se souvient :

« Lorsque tu m'as trouvée, maître, j'étais un dragonneau à peine éclos. Sans toi, je serais morte. Tu m'as nourrie, tu m'as soignée. Tu m'as parlé, surtout. Je t'ai compris, et tu m'as comprise. Peu d'humains sont capables de communiquer avec les dragons. Toi, tu as su tout de suite. »

Selka allonge le cou et pose la tête sur la

tombe étincelante. À travers le diamant, elle devine le corps du vieil homme, dans son habit de dragonnier, son visage blanc, ses yeux clos. Selka ferme les yeux, comme lui, et elle songe :

«Quand j'ai compris que tu allais mourir, maître, j'ai pensé mourir, moi aussi. Tu étais le premier des dragonniers. Et je croyais que tu vivrais des centaines et des centaines d'années, comme nous, les dragons.»

La dragonne se redresse et déploie ses ailes, qui prennent des reflets émeraude dans la clarté de l'aube. Elle se remémore sa dernière conversation avec messire Damian, tandis qu'elle l'emportait sur son dos vers le Royaume des Dragons.

«Le jeune Cham a su parler avec toi, Selka, a dit le vieil homme. Il est aussi doué que sa mère Dhydra; il sera un grand ami des dragons. Si la guerre éclate, il combattra pour le royaume d'Ombrune. Nour, le dragonneau qu'il a élevé, lui apportera toute son aide. Mais il aura besoin aussi de la tienne.»

«Que veux-tu que je fasse pour lui, maître?»

«Tu ne devines pas?»

«Que... je lui procure un dragon?»

«Oui, Selka. Et tu ne devras pas attendre neuf ans pour cela.»

«Il est encore si jeune...»

«Il l'est. Mais ne l'as-tu pas appelé toi-même "petit dragonnier"?»

«C'est vrai, maître. J'ai senti le lien

profond qui existe entre lui et les dragons. Cependant…»

Messire Damian a levé une main ridée:

«Pas de "cependant", Selka! Le royaume d'Ombrune devra bientôt affronter les Addraks, nous le savons tous les deux. Il faudra alors que Cham ait un dragon à chevaucher dans la bataille. Promets-moi, le moment venu, de lui offrir un de tes petits.»

«Je te le promets, maître.»

«C'est bien. Je peux mourir en paix.»

Messire Damian s'est alors allongé contre le cou de la dragonne et l'a laissée l'emporter. En lui-même il a songé:

«Ainsi, je n'aurai pas menti à cet enfant…»

Car, sur l'île aux Dragons, dans la tente qu'on avait dressée pour lui, n'a-t-il pas dit à Cham: «Voilà une belle rencontre: le plus jeune et le plus vieux des dragonniers»?

Aux premières heures du jour, un alcyon voyageur quitte l'île aux Dragons, porteur d'un message. L'oiseau revient avant midi avec la réponse:

*Nous nous réjouissons d'accueillir
le jeune Cham à la dragonnerie.
Le dragonnier Yénor viendra le chercher
demain matin.
Messire Onys, Maître Dragonnier.*

Pour la troisième fois en quelques mois, le garçon boucle son bagage. Et il se prépare à une longue absence. En tant qu'écuyer de Yénor, il va entamer sa formation de dragonnier. Ça ne se fera pas en un jour ! Quand reverra-t-il sa maison, sa sœur, ses parents ? À cette idée, sa poitrine se serre.

Sa mère entre alors dans sa chambre. Elle porte des vêtements pliés :

— Tiens ! Je t'ai cousu quelques chemises et des pantalons. Ceux que tu avais sont devenus trop petits ; tu as beaucoup grandi, ces temps-ci !

— Merci, maman.

Cham a dit ces mots sans beaucoup de conviction. Dhydra saisit le garçon par le menton et l'oblige à la regarder dans les yeux :

42

— Je comprends ce que tu ressens. C'est
dur de quitter sa famille, de commencer une
nouvelle vie. Pourtant, c'est à ce prix que
l'on devient soi-même. Tu es encore bien
jeune, et ce qu'on exige de toi est difficile.
Mais tu es fort, tu l'as prouvé. Travaille
avec persévérance. Apprends la langue des
dragons, elle est la base de toute magie.

Quant à ta formation de chevaucheur de dragons, tu en sais déjà davantage que les dragonniers du palais.

Elle lève un doigt et ajoute en souriant :

— Mais efforce-toi de rester modeste ! Ces hommes d'expérience pourraient s'irriter qu'un gamin leur fasse la leçon.

Cham lui sourit en retour, mi-inquiet mi-flatté :

— Je ferai de mon mieux, maman. Mais…

À voix basse, il avoue :

— … tu vas me manquer.

Dhydra attire le garçon contre elle et pose la joue contre ses cheveux :

— Toi aussi, tu vas me manquer, Cham.

Elle conclut avec gravité :

— J'aurais tant aimé me consacrer aux simples travaux de la ferme, ici, avec vous trois. Oublier un peu mes devoirs de magicienne. Hélas ! Le danger menace ; le royaume d'Ombrune a besoin de nous. Comme moi, tu accompliras ta tâche de tout ton cœur. Tu me le promets, mon fils ?

— Je te le promets, maman.

La nuit tombe sur l'île aux Dragons, sur Ombrune et, par-delà les Montagnes du Nord, sur le Territoire des Addraks. Le croissant de lune qui dérive dans le ciel n'est plus tout à fait aussi mince que la nuit précédente. Dans les profondeurs de la Citadelle Noire, il y a une salle secrète où douze personnages attendent, debout, immobiles. À la lueur des torches – des torches magiques qui ne s'éteignent pas –, on dirait douze statues. Leurs bouches sont muettes, leurs membres rigides, leurs esprits engourdis. Pourtant, si quelqu'un posait l'oreille contre les poitrines de pierre, il entendrait les douze cœurs qui battent, qui battent, qui battent…

Une menace dans le ciel

Yénor fixe la selle sur le dos de Nour : le Maître Dragonnier l'envoie sur l'île aux Dragons. Il ramènera Cham le matin même à la dragonnerie, et le garçon sera désormais son écuyer. C'est un honneur pour Yénor ; cela prouve que messire Onys l'estime capable de former un futur dragonnier. En vérité, le jeune homme ne s'en réjouit qu'à moitié. Cham n'est pas un gamin comme les autres, tout le monde le dit, à Nalsara. Il parle aux dragons, il pratique la magie. Il a été emprisonné dans la Citadelle Noire des Addraks et s'en est échappé. Pas tout seul, c'est vrai, mais tout de même… Yénor n'est dragonnier que depuis quelques mois. Qu'enseignera-t-il à un écuyer qui en sait plus que lui? Décidément, cette situation le met mal à l'aise.

Lâchant un petit nuage de fumée blanche, Nour lui souffle en pensée:

« Tout ira bien, tu verras ! »

Si son dragonnier n'entend pas vraiment ses paroles, il perçoit au moins des impressions. En effet, il lui flatte amicalement l'encolure:

– Tu cherches à me rassurer, hein?

Le dragon cligne des paupières, amusé:

« Oui, Yénor, tu as compris. Oh, ce ne sera pas toujours facile ! Cham a… du caractère. Mais ça se passera bien, j'y veillerai. »

Le jeune homme enfourche sa monture. Alors qu'ils décollent et virent au-dessus du palais pour s'élancer vers la mer, Yénor lâche entre ses dents:

– Il n'empêche ! Ça ne sera pas toujours facile. Ce gamin a un sale caractère…

«Ce n'est pas exactement ce que j'ai dit!» glousse Nour.

Cette fois, Yénor ne saisit pas. Pour lui, le curieux bruit de gorge émis par le dragon n'est qu'un grondement sans signification. On l'étonnerait beaucoup en lui révélant que les dragons savent rire!

Cham est prêt au départ. Son bagage est posé près de la porte d'entrée, il a pris le petit déjeuner avec sa sœur et ses parents. Il n'a plus qu'à attendre l'arrivée de Yénor. Ça l'ennuie un peu de devenir l'écuyer d'un dragonnier de dix-huit ans. Il aurait préféré quelqu'un de plus âgé, avec de l'expérience. Quoique… Yénor est le dragonnier de Nour! Cham travaillera chaque jour aux côtés du dragon aux yeux d'or, qu'il a vu naître dans la grange. C'était il y a sept mois. Il s'en est passé, des choses, en sept mois!

Cham se poste devant la fenêtre de la cuisine et contemple le ciel gris, d'où la créature ailée va bientôt surgir.

Son père vient le rejoindre. Entourant d'un bras les épaules de son fils, il dit :

— Tu te souviens de ton premier vol sur le dos de Nour ? De votre atterrissage en catastrophe au beau milieu de la cour ?

Cham hoche la tête :

— Si je m'en souviens ! Tu m'avais interdit de le faire ; tu étais furieux.

— Il y avait de quoi ! Nour n'était encore qu'un dragonneau. Il aurait pu se briser une patte.

Oui, c'était une bêtise, mais Cham ne regrette rien ; ce premier vol à moitié raté lui a appris une chose importante : quand on s'est fixé un but, il faut tout faire pour y parvenir.

— Ce jour-là, dit-il gravement, j'ai su que je deviendrais dragonnier.

Son père lui ébouriffe les cheveux :

— Tâche d'abord d'être un bon écuyer ! Au fond, soigner les dragons ou les cochons…

— Oh, papa ! Ce n'est pas du tout pareil !

Antos s'esclaffe, et Cham pouffe à son tour, comprenant que son père le taquine. Ça lui fait du bien de rire ; il est un peu nerveux.

Il entend derrière lui des bruits de vais-
selle qu'on remue. Bien que la cuisine soit
déjà rangée, sa mère et sa sœur vont et viennent, déplaçant une pile de bols, donnant un
coup de torchon sur la table. Elles aussi sont
nerveuses. Cham s'en va, et son absence
risque d'être longue.

Soudain, une énorme masse verte apparaît et se pose devant la maison dans un
bruissement d'ailes. Le garçon se précipite
au-dehors :

— Nour !

Saisissant des deux mains la tête de la
créature, il appuie le front contre les douces
écailles de son museau :

— Nour... Je suis content de te revoir.

Cham est parti.

Nyne reste un long moment au bord de la
falaise, jusqu'à ce que le grand dragon ne soit
plus qu'un point vert dans le ciel gris. Elle
vient à peine de retrouver son frère, et le voilà
qui s'en va encore. Pour combien de temps ?

Le vent est froid; la petite fille resserre son châle autour d'elle. Allons, elle ne peut pas s'attarder ici. C'est l'heure de distribuer le grain aux poules.

Alors qu'elle fait demi-tour pour regagner la maison, Nyne s'immobilise. Elle tend l'oreille, intriguée : dans le grondement des vagues cognant contre les rochers, il lui semble entendre de mystérieuses paroles.

Une drôle de pensée lui vient :

« Les élusims ! Ils discutent entre eux, quelque part, dans leur royaume marin ! Que se disent-ils ? »

Elle écoute, mais ne saisit rien. Cependant, elle est un peu consolée.

« Vag, songe-t-elle. Mon ami Vag ! Tu ne m'as pas oubliée, n'est-ce pas ? Tu viendras si j'ai besoin de toi. »

À peine Nour a-t-il décollé que Cham oublie toutes ses inquiétudes. Il voyage à dos de dragon ! Là, dans le ciel, avec la mer houleuse roulant ses vagues en contrebas, il se sent à sa place. Certes, pour l'instant, il partage la selle de Yénor. Un jour, il sera seul dans les airs avec son propre dragon. Un jour, mais… quand ?

La voix de Nour résonne alors à l'intérieur de son crâne :

« Peut-être bien plus tôt que tu ne l'imagines, petit maître ! »

Le garçon rouspète mentalement :

« Dis donc ! Tu t'introduis dans mes pensées, maintenant ? »

« Parfois, tu penses si fort qu'on doit t'entendre jusqu'au Royaume des Dragons ! » commente Nour, moqueur.

À cet instant, le garçon tressaille. Devant lui, le ciel s'est brusquement obscurci. De sombres nuées s'enroulent, tourbillonnent, traversées d'éclairs fourchus.

« Nour ! s'exclame Cham, alarmé. Qu'est-ce que c'est ? Est-ce… la strige ? »

Plusieurs secondes passent avant qu'il perçoive la réponse :

«Non, la strige est loin d'ici, dans le Territoire des Addraks. Ce n'est pas elle ; ce n'est qu'une image de sa colère et de son impatience.»

«Comment ça ?»

«Elle sait que tu reviens au palais. Or, pour le moment, elle ne peut rien faire, car Darkat, son maître, est changé en statue.»

«C'est vrai, se souvient Cham. La pierre de Semblance, le sort de pétrification que Nastrad a lancé sur les sorciers...»

L'étrange phénomène se dissipe aussi vite qu'il s'est formé. Derrière le garçon, Yénor lance avec gaieté :

— On est presque arrivés. Regarde ! On voit déjà les tours du palais. La traversée est plus rapide à dos de dragon qu'en bateau, hein ?

— C'est sûr, acquiesce Cham.

Étonné, il s'adresse à Nour :

«Et Yénor ? Il n'a pas vu ces espèces de nuages... ?»

«Non, il n'a rien vu. Il n'est pas magicien, lui.»

Avec un gloussement, Nour conclut :

«Il n'est pas dragon non plus!»

Mise à l'épreuve

Cham est de très mauvaise humeur.
Depuis quatre jours qu'il est à la dragonnerie, il a l'impression qu'on le prend
pour un valet. Certes, il s'occupe de Nour.
Dès l'aube, il vient remplir son abreuvoir,
nettoyer son box, lui astiquer les griffes.
Mais il a vite terminé.

Le reste de la journée, on le charge de
quantité de travaux plus ennuyeux les uns
que les autres : aider les bouchers à découper
la viande pour le repas des dragons, apporter
du bois aux cuisines, balayer la cour, vider

les seaux d'eau sale… Ce n'est pas ainsi qu'il s'était imaginé le rôle d'un écuyer! D'ailleurs, que font-ils, les autres écuyers? Il y en a cinq, tous bien plus âgés que lui. Eux, ils sont presque constamment en compagnie de leur dragonnier; on ne les emploie pas comme domestiques!

Ce qui déprime le plus Cham, c'est qu'à son arrivée, messire Onys a à peine pris le temps de l'accueillir.

– Ah, te voilà! a dit le Maître Dragonnier quand le garçon s'est présenté dans son bureau. Ta formation va commencer; j'espère que tu t'appliqueras. Maintenant, petit, va rejoindre Yénor, j'ai du travail.

Et le vieil homme a replongé le nez dans ses papiers.

Après cela, Cham a croisé son ami Hadal dans un corridor, une pile de dossiers sous le bras. À son tour, celui-ci lui a lancé:

– Ah, te voilà! Content de te voir! On bavardera plus tard, hein? J'ai du travail!

Et le secrétaire de messire Onys a filé, l'air pressé.

Quant à Isendrine et Mélisande, elles n'ont même pas daigné venir le saluer. Sans doute les magiciennes avaient-elles du travail, elles aussi !

Poussant une lourde brouette chargée de linge sale qu'il doit porter aux lavandières, Cham marmonne entre ses dents :

– Si j'avais su, je serais resté à la ferme !

Pendant ce temps, Yénor est avec les autres dragonniers. À cause de la guerre qui menace, ils décollent chaque matin sur leurs dragons et filent s'entraîner au-dessus de la campagne. Au cours d'un combat, savoir se tenir en selle dans n'importe quelle position peut leur sauver la vie.

Le lavoir est à l'extérieur du palais ; sur le sentier, le garçon passe devant un grand pin. Ses branches, régulièrement disposées, donnent envie d'y grimper.

« De là-haut, se dit Cham, je verrai peut-être les dragonniers… »

Aussitôt, il abandonne son chargement et entame l'escalade.

En effet, depuis la cime de l'arbre, il aperçoit entre les branches le ballet coloré des dragons dans le ciel. Ils s'exercent à virer sur l'aile, à piquer vers le sol avant de remonter en flèche, à voler la tête en bas et à exécuter quantité de voltiges. Cham repère vite Nour. Le jeune dragon est le plus élégant de tous, son vol est souple, gracieux. Mais Cham voit bien qu'il évite les mouvements brusques, qu'il ne s'élance jamais à pleine vitesse.

« Yénor n'est pas encore un bon chevaucheur de dragon », comprend le garçon.

Ça le fait sourire et, en même temps, ça l'irrite. Lui, s'il était sur le dos de Nour, ce ne sont pas quelques acrobaties qui lui feraient peur… !

– Qu'est-ce que tu fabriques là-haut, toi ? lance alors une voix de femme.

Cham sursaute. Allons bon ! Si ça se trouve, il va être puni. Il ne manquerait plus que ça ! Il se dépêche de descendre de son perchoir. Alors, la femme éclate de rire :

– Cham ! Je ne t'avais pas reconnu. C'est Viriana !

Le garçon se jette dans ses bras.

Enfin quelqu'un prend le temps de bavarder avec lui, de l'interroger sur ses premiers jours au palais ! Cham en a gros sur le cœur. Il commence à conter ses malheurs à la servante. Cette femme qui a élevé sa mère est un peu sa grand-mère.

Viriana le tire alors derrière le tronc du grand pin et lui confie une chose qui le laisse stupéfait :

– Cachons-nous, mon enfant ! Je ne devrais pas te raconter ça, mais on m'a interdit de te parler. J'ai ordre d'attendre une semaine avant de venir te voir.

– Interdit de… ? Ça, par exemple ! Pourquoi ?

La vieille femme hausse les épaules :

– On ne me l'a pas expliqué. J'ai tout de même ma petite idée !

Elle adresse au garçon un sourire malicieux :

– On te met à l'épreuve, voilà pourquoi !

Cham s'étonne :

– À l'épreuve ? Je ne comprends pas.

– C'est simple : tu es un enfant très… particulier. Tu es le fils d'une grande magicienne, tu communiques avec les dragons, tu es exceptionnellement doué pour la magie. Mais tu n'as pas onze ans…

– Je vais les avoir dans quelques jours.

– C'est vrai. Onze ans, cependant, c'est encore très jeune. Et on compte sur toi pour défendre le royaume contre les Addraks. Aussi, messire Onys, les magiciennes, tous craignent que… Comment dire ?

Cham devine :

– Que je me croie plus malin que tout le monde ? Ils veulent voir si je supporte d'être traité comme… un simple valet de ferme sans me décourager ? C'est ça ?

Le sourire de Viriana s'élargit, et un soleil de rides s'épanouit au coin de ses yeux :

– C'est ça.

Le garçon soupire :

– Eh bien, merci, Viriana ! Sans toi, j'aurais peut-être piqué une colère, jeté un seau d'eau à la tête de Yénor ou fait une bêtise de ce genre ! À présent que je suis prévenu, je vais me tenir à carreau. Ils n'en reviendront pas, je te le promets !

La servante lui révèle :

– De toute façon, cette mise à l'épreuve prend fin dans trois jours. Ce ne sera pas trop difficile. Allez, va vite ! N'arrive pas en retard au lavoir,

on t'accuserait d'avoir traîné en route, pour…
t'amuser à grimper aux arbres, par exemple !

Tous deux éclatent de rire. Puis Cham
reprend sa brouette de linge, pendant que
Viriana patiente un peu avant de repartir,
pour être sûre qu'on ne les surprenne pas
ensemble.

Vers le milieu de l'après-midi, Cham
brosse la pierre d'un abreuvoir dans la cour
de la dragonnerie. Il y met toute son énergie
et s'amuse même à chantonner. Personne ne
pourra prétendre qu'il ne met pas de cœur à
l'ouvrage !

Soudain, un éclair de lumière lui fait
lever la tête. Une fenêtre vient de s'ouvrir,
celle du bureau de messire Onys, et le soleil
s'est reflété sur la vitre.

Cham distingue alors trois silhouettes,
dans l'encadrement de la fenêtre : Isendrine,
Mélisande et le Maître Dragonnier. On
dirait que… Oui, c'est bien lui qu'ils regar-
dent ! Ils parlent de lui, c'est sûr !

Le garçon est pris d'une folle curiosité :

que se disent-ils ? Il voudrait bien le savoir.

C'est alors qu'une idée lui vient.

Cham achève son nettoyage en déversant un seau d'eau sur la pierre. Puis il se dirige en sifflotant vers un coin de la cour, où les trois personnages à la fenêtre ne le verront pas. Là, il se concentre, se souvenant de sa première leçon avec Isendrine et Mélisande : pour prononcer un terme de magie, lui ont-elles expliqué, il faut d'abord s'emplir d'air les poumons et le cerveau. On lâche ensuite le mot en expirant, ni trop lentement, ni trop vite. Depuis, le garçon a eu l'occasion de s'entraîner, avec sa mère, et aussi... avec Darkat. Ça, il aimerait mieux l'oublier. Pourtant, le jeune sorcier addrak lui a enseigné des choses qui pourront se révéler utiles.

En tout cas, pour l'instant, pas question de magie noire. Il veut se servir d'un sortilège que lui a appris sa mère. S'il en est capable... ! Car il n'a jamais tenté de le lancer seul.

Cham inspire à fond, fixe son esprit sur

la formule à prononcer. Enfin il souffle en articulant :

– *Borodié !*

Dans la seconde qui suit, il a l'impression que le sol monte d'un coup à sa rencontre. Le mur, à côté de lui, est devenu une falaise ; il en aperçoit à peine le sommet. Il a réussi ! Il s'est transformé en moineau !

En quelques coups d'ailes, il vole vers le rebord de la fenêtre, dont messire Onys et les deux femmes aux cheveux rouges se sont écartés. Ils discutent à présent, debout au milieu de la pièce. Cham allonge son petit cou d'oiseau pour ne pas perdre une miette de leur conversation.

Le Maître Dragonnier achève une phrase dont le garçon n'a pas entendu le début. Cependant, c'est clair : on parle bel et bien de lui :

– … ne se comporte pas si mal, à ce qu'on m'a dit.

– Il doit pourtant être blessé…

– … dans sa fierté, commentent les magiciennes.

Messire Onys hoche la tête, pensif :

– Je trouve cette épreuve un peu cruelle.
Mais le roi Bertram y tenait.

Isendrine et Mélisande avouent en riant :

– Le roi n'y a pas pensé tout seul !
C'est…

– … nous qui lui avons soufflé l'idée.

– Vraiment, belles dames ? Enfin, dans
trois jours, ce sera terminé.

Les magiciennes échangent un coup d'œil
complice avant d'ajouter :

– Oh, ça se termine aujourd'hui même, car…

– … le jeune Cham est au courant, à présent !

Pivotant d'un même mouvement vers la fenêtre, elles lancent :

– Tu peux reprendre ta forme humaine, petit moineau ! Tu…

– … t'es montré plus malin que nous ! Bravo !

Alors, l'oiseau gris posé sur le rebord grandit d'un coup, et c'est un garçon qui saute dans la pièce, sous le regard ahuri de messire Onys.

Impatience

Très loin, par-delà les Montagnes du Nord, la Citadelle Noire des Addraks se dresse au sommet d'une falaise à pic. Le bruit sourd des vagues s'écrasant contre le roc ébranle la forteresse ; il résonne jusque dans la salle secrète où les douze sorciers changés en pierre patientent. Mais, au fond de son antre, la strige s'agite. Voilà des jours que son maître n'est pas venu la voir. La créature sait quelle force l'en empêche. Elle a reconnu la magie qui emprisonne le jeune sorcier. Cette magie, elle l'a déjà flairée. Dans le marécage. Au pied des Mornes Monts. La nuit où des serpents géants ont attaqué son maître. Il en a été épouvanté. Pas elle. Les serpents n'étaient qu'une illusion. Un sortilège destiné à cacher la fuite de la femme et du garçon. Ceux-là, la strige les hait.

À ce souvenir, elle prend elle-même la forme d'un serpent ; elle roule et déroule ses anneaux de fumée, furieuse d'être enfermée, impuissante. Elle projette avec violence l'image de sa colère vers Nalsara.

Après le retour de son maître à la citadelle, elle s'est pourtant réjouie d'emporter les douze sorciers jusqu'au marécage. À eux tous, pensait-elle, ils résisteraient aux maléfices. Ils retrouveraient les fugitifs, ils les ramèneraient dans leur cachot. Mais rien ne s'est passé comme l'âme noire de la créature l'attendait. Les sorciers ont rapporté la pierre-qu'il-ne-faut-pas-toucher. La strige a tenté d'avertir son maître. Il n'a pas voulu entendre. À présent, la pierre maléfique l'a rendu sourd, aveugle et insensible. Il vit encore, cependant. Il vit. Et il se vengera.

Quand messire Onys est remis de sa surprise, il éclate de rire :

– Cham, tu es vraiment un garçon étonnant ! L'épreuve qu'on t'imposait est donc terminée, j'en suis bien content. À mon avis, c'était du temps perdu. Tu es ici pour être écuyer, pas valet. On aurait mieux fait de te mettre tout de suite à l'entraînement. Car, malgré tes dons exceptionnels, tu as encore beaucoup à apprendre, et...

« Je le sais, que j'ai encore à apprendre, pense Cham. On n'arrête pas de me le répéter... »

Agacé, il laisse son regard errer au-dehors. Il aperçoit alors une nuée noire, au-dessus des toits de la dragonnerie. La masse nuageuse s'allonge, s'étale ; un éclair en jaillit. Puis elle tourbillonne sur elle-même et disparaît.

– ... puisque tu dois approfondir ta connaissance de la langue des dragons, continue le Maître Dragonnier, il faut que...

– La strige ! le coupe le garçon, qui n'a pas écouté. Vous avez vu ? La strige se manifeste. J'ai déjà assisté à ce phénomène avec Nour, pendant qu'il me ramenait à Nalsara.

— Oui, admet Isendrine, il se produit régulièrement depuis que les Addraks…

— … ont été pétrifiés, poursuit Mélisande. La créature garde un œil sur nous.

Elles ont parlé d'un ton calme, mais le jeune écuyer a senti leur trouble.

— D'après Nour, dit-il, ce n'est qu'une image de son impatience et de sa colère.

Les magiciennes acquiescent sans rien ajouter. Messire Onys hausse un sourcil :

— Vous ne m'avez pas parlé de ça. Est-ce alarmant ?

Après un temps de silence, les dames aux cheveux rouges déclarent :

– Lorsque colère tourne en rage…

– … impatience éclate en orage.

À ces mots, un frisson désagréable court sur la peau du garçon. Il imagine trop bien à quoi ressemble ce genre d'orage ! Il n'en a eu que trop d'exemples !

Les magiciennes s'adressent alors à lui :

– Et quand la pierre redeviendra chair, magie noire…

– … et magie blanche iront de pair.

– De pair ? répète Cham, perplexe.

– Ça signifie qu'il est grand temps que tu t'exerces à la magie ! lâche messire Onys. Alors, assez de corvées inutiles ! Mesdames, je compte sur vous pour prendre en main la formation de notre nouvel écuyer !

Le garçon cache un sourire : il n'avait encore jamais vu le Maître Dragonnier s'énerver ! Il est vrai que les magiciennes, avec leur drôle de façon de parler, sont parfois exaspérantes.

Depuis cette conversation, Isendrine et Mélisande font monter Cham chaque jour, dès le lever du soleil, au sommet d'une tour. Celle où, deux mois plus tôt, elles lui ont donné sa première leçon de magie. D'un côté, on domine la mer. De l'autre, par-delà les dernières maisons de la cité, c'est la campagne, avec ses champs, ses vergers, ses forêts. Dès qu'il arrive en haut, le garçon tâche d'apercevoir les Montagnes du Nord, très loin à l'horizon. Là-bas, le Libre Peuple survit, enfermé dans ses grottes secrètes...

Ce matin encore, accoudé au parapet, il a une pensée pour Igrid et son grand-père, Nastrad, le vieux chaman. Il aimerait tant la revoir, la jolie rouquine ! Elle l'a pourtant souvent taquiné. Quant à Nastrad, il a promis son alliance avec Ombrune en cas de conflit avec les Addraks. Cham en vient presque à souhaiter la guerre rien que pour retrouver Igrid.

– La guerre viendra bien assez tôt, et...

– ... ta formation a pris du retard, déclarent les magiciennes.

Cham se retourne d'un bloc et leur jette un regard noir. Oh, ces deux-là! Elles ne vont pas, elles aussi, lire dans ses pensées!

– Elle aurait pu commencer plus tôt, ma formation! rétorque-t-il. Au lieu de ça, j'ai transporté des seaux d'eau, j'ai lavé des carrelages…

Les femmes l'interrompent d'un geste de la main:

– Sans l'impatience où tu étais, aurais-tu…

– … trouvé en toi la capacité de te transformer en oiseau?

– Je…, commence le garçon.

Elles ne le laissent pas poursuivre:

– Tout est apprentissage à qui est assez sage. Et, maintenant…

– … au travail!

Sous la direction de ses deux préceptrices, Cham s'exerce à faire apparaître des objets. Isendrine et Mélisande lui apprennent les mots à prononcer, et le garçon s'efforce de les ranger dans sa mémoire avec ceux qu'il connaît déjà: *Krandach'*, par exemple, qui signifie bâton. C'est le premier que les magiciennes lui ont appris. Il y a aussi *Brilill'iol,* qui donne de la lumière. Lorsque la strige l'a emporté dans les airs, Cham s'est servi de deux termes trouvés dans les pages d'un livre: avec *Swor*, il s'est procuré une épée et a fendu la masse nébuleuse de la créature. Il a alors sauté dans le vide en criant *Fennas!* «Des ailes!» Malheureusement, il était trop débutant pour lancer deux sorts à la suite. Il n'a pas oublié ce moment terrible: l'épée s'est dissoute dans sa main, et il est tombé comme une pierre. Si la strige ne l'avait pas rattrapé, il se serait écrasé au sol! Au lieu de ça, il a été emprisonné dans la Citadelle Noire…

Tout est bien différent, maintenant. Cham enchaîne les formulations, sans oublier de régler sa respiration.

Ce matin-là, il s'exerce d'abord à des choses pratiques: *Klout* lui procure une clé capable d'ouvrir toutes les serrures; avec *Orgon'*, il allume un feu; *Shiniel* lui donne une pèlerine.

Le tissu magique ressemble à de la laine, il en a la chaleur. Le garçon est enchanté de sa réussite. Il s'enveloppe fièrement dans le vêtement qu'il vient de créer :

– Formidable ! Et comment fait-on pour avoir des bottes neuves ?

Au même instant, le chaud manteau s'évanouit en fumée.

Devant la mine déconfite de leur élève, les magiciennes pouffent :

– On te l'a déjà dit, petit ! Pour qu'un sortilège dure, il ne faut…

– … jamais cesser d'y croire !

– J'y croyais, pourtant…, grommelle Cham, vexé.

Isendrine et Mélisande échangent un regard faussement étonné :

– Peut-on croire à une pèlerine quand…

– … on a des bottes dans la tête ?

La suite de la leçon porte sur des sorts différents. Cham découvre que *Lidout draï* fera tomber la pluie, que *Miétit prax* changera la pierre en sable. Quant à la formule *Néoc niévidim*, que sa mère a utilisée lors de

leur fuite vers les marécages, elle le rendra invisible.

Au bout de trois heures d'entraînement, le garçon est épuisé. Il a l'impression que son crâne va exploser. Soudain, la tête lui tourne. Pris de vertige, il titube jusqu'au parapet de pierre, s'y accroche. Un tourbillon de vent le frappe au visage, il ferme les yeux et…

Et il s'envole.

Le temps se fait court

Cham vole. Il chevauche un dragon blanc dont les écailles ont des reflets d'argent. Dans un lent battement d'ailes, le dragon fend l'air en silence. Il monte jusqu'aux nuages, redescend en piqué, et des rafales glacées fouettent le visage du garçon. Puis sa monture plane au-dessus d'une campagne verdoyante, frôle la cime des arbres d'une épaisse forêt. Une barre rocheuse apparaît, au loin. Le dragon file droit vers elle. Le garçon reconnaît ces pentes abruptes, ces sommets couronnés de neige : les Montagnes du Nord !

La voix du dragon retentit alors dans sa tête : « Bientôt, nous les franchirons ensemble ! »

Cham balbutie :

– Qui… Qui es-tu ?

« Quelle question ! Je suis ton dragon, tu le sais. Il y a déjà longtemps que, dans tes rêves, tu m'as donné un nom. »

Le cœur du garçon bondit dans sa poitrine :

– Tu es Cyd !

« Oui, Cham, je suis Cyd. »

Un tourbillon de vent les enveloppe tous les deux, emportant avec lui cette unique syllabe, à la fois douce et dure : Cyd, Cyd…

Quand l'apprenti magicien reprend conscience, il est allongé sur le sol de pierre. Il reconnaît les visages des magiciennes penchées sur lui.

Le prenant chacune par une main, elles l'aident à se relever. Encore mal assuré sur ses pieds, il murmure :

— Cyd...

— Un très beau nom...

— ... pour un dragon, approuvent-elles.

Cham écarquille les yeux, interloqué :

— Comment avez-vous deviné... ?

Sa surprise fait sourire les dames aux cheveux rouges :

— Ton corps est resté sur la tour, mais ton esprit a voyagé...

— ... dans l'avenir. Et, dans ton avenir, il y a forcément un dragon.

Le garçon s'approche du parapet. Songeur, il contemple la mer miroitante. Enfin, il demande :

— Était-ce un avenir... lointain ?

— Pas si lointain, Cham. Non, pas...

— ... si lointain.

— Donc, je vais bientôt être...

Il n'ose pas prononcer le mot.

Les magiciennes poussent un long soupir. Puis elles lâchent :

– Dragonnier ? Oui, hélas ! Car ta vision est…

– … un nouveau présage de guerre.

Dans l'île aux Dragons, Nyne découvre le bonheur d'avoir une maman. Et Dhydra est une merveilleuse maman ! Elle est belle, elle est tendre et gaie, et… elle prépare des plats délicieux ! Mais surtout, elle est toujours prête à écouter sa fille, à répondre à ses incessantes questions.

En cette fin d'après-midi un peu fraîche, elles se sont installées toutes les deux dans la cuisine, près de la cheminée. Dhydra coud une robe à Nyne, qui s'exerce à ourler un morceau de vieux drap pour en faire un torchon.

– Plus serrés, tes points ! intervient Dhydra. Pique ton aiguille comme ça, regarde !

La petite fille hoche la tête et s'applique, en sortant le bout de la langue.

Elle travaille un instant en silence. Il y a encore tant de questions qu'elle aimerait poser ! Enfin, elle demande :

– Maman, ton miroir, comment tu l'as eu ?

– C'est un cadeau de Selka.

Nyne reste l'aiguille en l'air, interloquée :

– De Selka ?

– Lorsque j'avais ton âge, messire Damian a découvert que je parlais avec les dragons. C'est pourquoi il m'a engagée à la Dragonnerie royale.

– Oui, il nous l'a raconté, à Cham et moi, quand il est venu sur l'île avant de... de partir vers le Royaume des Dragons. Et, un jour, il t'a emmenée dans l'île, pour voir s'il y avait des bébés dragons. Il y en avait deux, mais ils étaient morts.

– Ça m'a bouleversée, tu penses !

Dhydra ajoute, rêveuse :

– Aussi, plus tard, quand j'ai rencontré ce beau garçon qui allait être votre père, je l'ai convaincu de s'installer ici, dans l'île, et de s'occuper des dragonneaux, pour qu'ils survivent après être sortis de l'œuf.

– Et papa est devenu le Grand Éleveur du royaume ! Mais, Selka ?

– Selka, comme tu le sais, était la dragonne de messire Damian. Un soir, je devais avoir onze ans, elle nous a emmenés sur la plage, tous les deux. Elle disait vouloir nous offrir un cadeau.

La jeune femme s'interrompt, le temps d'enfiler son aiguille.

– Un cadeau? la relance Nyne.

– Nous avons suivi Selka un long moment. J'ai compris ensuite qu'elle voulait être loin du palais, pour que personne ne nous voie.

– Ah? fait la petite fille, qui n'en peut plus de curiosité.

– Là, la dragonne a soufflé par deux fois un jet de flammes sur le sable. Et le sable a fondu, il s'est transformé en verre.

– Oooooooh!

– En remuant la pâte de verre du bout de ses griffes, Selka a façonné deux objets, un pour son dragonnier et un pour moi.

Nyne s'exclame :

– Une boule de verre pour messire Damian : le cristal-qui-voit, qu'il a donné à Cham ! Et le miroir pour toi !

L'enthousiasme de la fillette amuse Dhydra :

– Eh oui ! Le souffle de feu des dragons est chargé de magie. Voilà pourquoi ces objets ont autant de pouvoir.

La mère et la fille se remettent à leur couture. Puis Nyne reprend :

– Mais… pourquoi as-tu donné ton miroir à messire Damian ?

– Quand je me suis installée dans l'île avec ton père, je ne voulais plus être magicienne. J'espérais simplement vivre avec l'homme que j'aimais, élever mes enfants. Les Addraks en ont décidé autrement. Un jour de tempête, j'ai cru entendre un appel de dragon, sur la falaise. Tu connais la suite.

– L'affreuse strige t'a enlevée.

Nyne a parlé à voix basse. Elle n'aime pas prononcer le nom du monstre. Les mains un peu tremblantes, elle enfonce l'aiguille dans le tissu.

— Aïe !

Elle porte à la bouche son doigt où perle une goutte de sang.

— Tu t'es piquée ?

Dhydra pose son ouvrage et lui tend les bras. La petite fille s'y jette ; elle serre sa mère de toutes ses forces en murmurant :

— Maman ! Oh, maman ! Tu ne nous quitteras plus jamais, hein, maman ?

Très loin de là, dans le Royaume des Dragons, Selka a été convoquée par le Conseil des Anciens. L'un d'eux, Nâhl, prend la parole :

« Le temps se fait court. Plus que quatre nuits, et la lune sera pleine. »

« La nouvelle lune, murmure Selka. Les effets de la pierre de Semblance cesseront. Et les sorciers seront libérés du sortilège… »

Tous les dragons approuvent gravement.

Nâhl continue :

« Certes, les Addraks ne décideront pas tout de suite d'attaquer Ombrune. Leur armée n'est pas assez puissante, ils le savent. Mais… »

Il lâche un long soupir, et un jet de fumée grise sort de ses naseaux.

C'est un autre Ancien qui poursuit :

« Mais, si la pierre de Semblance les a pétrifiés, elle n'a pas paralysé leurs capacités magiques, au contraire. »

Selka allonge le cou, intriguée :

« Comment ça ? »

« Ils sont en train d'absorber une partie de son énergie. Ils la concentrent dans la main ou le pied de pierre que chacun d'entre eux conservera. Cela va encore augmenter leurs pouvoirs. »

« Et leur magie noire sera plus redoutable que jamais, conclut Nâhl. Ils pourraient bien imaginer un mauvais tour… »

« Un mauvais tour ? répète Selka. Comme de créer une deuxième strige ? »

« Peut-être. À moins qu'ils n'inventent

quelque chose de pire. C'est pourquoi nous devons intervenir. Rappelez-vous ce qui s'est passé à Norlande, il y a trois siècles ! À cette époque, nous n'avions pas de relations avec les humains. Puis, il y a environ cent cinquante ans, nous avons décidé de secourir le royaume d'Ombrune, pour qu'il ne tombe pas à son tour sous la domination des Addraks. Mais sans intervenir directement dans les affaires des humains. »

L'autre Ancien hoche la tête :

« C'est pourquoi, tous les neuf ans, nous avons envoyé une ou deux de nos dragonnes déposer un œuf, sur l'île, au large de Nalsara. Nous savions que les humains mettraient du temps à découvrir les dragonneaux, qu'ils devraient ensuite apprendre à les élever. Au début, tous les petits nés sur l'île mouraient, hélas ! Le premier humain qui a su soigner un bébé dragon a aussi été le premier des dragonniers. »

Selka murmure, émue :

« Mon maître, messire Damian ! Et ce bébé dragon, c'était moi ! »

Nâhl conclut :

«Désormais, nous comptons parmi les humains de grands amis des dragons. Nous devons les soutenir dans leur combat. L'un d'eux, en particulier…»

Selka a compris. Néanmoins, elle demande :

«Qu'attendez-vous de moi ?»

«Que tu offres au jeune Cham un dragon à lui, ainsi que tu le lui as promis.»

«Je le lui ai promis, c'est vrai. Cependant, n'est-ce pas un peu tôt ? Il a encore si peu d'expérience…»

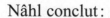

«C'est vrai, Selka, mais le temps se fait court, redit l'Ancien. Pour une fois, une éclosion aura lieu sur l'île moins d'un an après la précédente, et hors saison. Chez nous comme là-bas, nos petits naissent habituellement au plus chaud de l'été. Celui-ci devra s'accommoder de la fraîcheur du printemps. Il n'en sera que plus résistant!»

La dragonne incline sa tête verte:

«Très bien, Nâhl. Cham aura son dragon. Et ce sera le plus beau qu'aucun dragonnier ait possédé.»

Un nouveau crépuscule tombe sur le Royaume des Dragons, sur Ombrune, sur le Territoire des Addraks. Les étoiles s'allument une à une, tandis que la lune commence son lent voyage à travers le ciel. Seul un dernier morceau d'ombre mange encore sa face pâle. Plus que quatre nuits, et elle sera pleine, parfaitement ronde.

8

À dos de dragon

Pour Cham, finies les corvées! Non seulement il n'a plus à transporter des seaux d'eau ou à frotter des carrelages, mais messire Onys l'a même prié d'expliquer aux dragonniers comment mieux communiquer avec leurs dragons!

Parmi les vingt-sept hommes formant l'escadron volant de l'armée, quatre comprennent un peu leur monture. Yénor est fier d'être de ceux-là. Or, il ne saisit que quelques mots: «Oui, non, en selle, vite...» Pour le reste, il perçoit des impressions, rien de plus.

Lorsque Cham se retrouve face aux vingt-sept dragonniers, dont certains ont l'âge d'être son grand-père, il est très intimidé.

Il se gratte la gorge et commence :

— Messires, je vous parlerai de la façon de vous adresser à votre dragon. Mais je ne vous apprendrai pas à entendre sa voix. C'est un don qu'on a ou qu'on n'a pas.

À ces mots, une rumeur de mécontentement monte de l'assistance.

« Je n'aurais pas dû dire ça, pense Cham. Ils croient que je me vante… »

Embarrassé, il s'agite sur son siège, se rattrape comme il peut :

— Vous avez tous une longue expérience. Et messire Damian, que j'ai rencontré, vous a sûrement transmis beaucoup de son savoir.

— Messire Damian a été un grand dragonnier, intervient un imposant barbu qui a au moins quarante ans. Mais il était un peu fou, quand il s'agissait des dragons. Il prétendait, comme toi, converser avec eux ! Ce sont des bêtes intelligentes, je te l'accorde. De là à affirmer qu'elles connaissent notre langue…

Crois-tu que, si j'ordonne à ma Cyrna «À droite!», elle virera sans que j'aie besoin de tirer sur les rênes?

— Avez-vous essayé, messire?

— Je… Non.

Quelques rires s'élèvent. Encouragé, le garçon poursuit:

— Il n'est même pas nécessaire de parler tout haut. Il suffit de s'exprimer par la pensée.

— Les dragons captent nos pensées? s'exclame un homme aux longs cheveux blancs.

Avec une grimace, il ajoute:

— Alors, je comprends pourquoi Slovar a manqué me flanquer par terre, l'autre jour. Je l'avais traité mentalement de «saleté de bourricot».

Cette fois, tous s'esclaffent, et Cham retrouve son assurance:

— Ainsi, dans une bataille, vous pourrez diriger vos montures de la voix ou par la pensée. Et vos bras seront libres de manier lance, épée et bouclier.

— Que sais-tu des batailles, gamin? raille un costaud au crâne rasé.

Le garçon bafouille :

– Moi ? Rien, messire. Je… Je ne me suis jamais battu, je…

Il s'aperçoit alors que messire Onys vient d'entrer. Tous se lèvent et s'inclinent avec respect. Le Maître Dragonnier les invite d'un geste à se rasseoir. Puis il déclare :

– N'oubliez pas, messires, que, si vous êtes entraînés au maniement des armes, vous ne vous êtes jamais battus, vous non plus ! Depuis la Paix des Frontières, signée avec les Addraks voilà presque un siècle, notre royaume n'a pas connu la guerre. Cham n'est pas un combattant. Pas encore…

Il balaye l'assemblée d'un regard autoritaire avant de reprendre :

– Cependant le roi Bertram compte sur lui, malgré son extrême jeunesse. Car il possède un don rare. Seul notre regretté compagnon, messire Damian, avait une relation semblable avec les dragons. Il n'est plus là, hélas ! pour nous soutenir dans la guerre qui s'annonce. Mais, d'une certaine manière, c'est messire Damian lui-même qui a choisi ce « gamin », comme vous dites, pour le remplacer.

D'un ton bienveillant, il s'adresse à Cham :

— N'est-ce pas, mon garçon ?

Le jeune écuyer précise timidement :

— C'est d'abord Selka, sa dragonne, qui m'a… euh… parlé.

Une lueur de curiosité s'allume dans l'œil du Maître Dragonnier :

— Vraiment ? Et que t'a-t-elle dit ?

Cham se balance sur son siège, embarrassé. Il ne peut pas répondre à cette question devant cette assemblée, car, la première fois que Selka lui a parlé, elle l'a appelé « petit dragonnier » !

— Eh bien ? insiste le vieil homme.

Cham devient écarlate. Enfin il réplique avec fermeté :

— C'est un secret, messire.

Par chance, ce dernier n'insiste pas. Il se tourne de nouveau vers l'assemblée :

— Beaucoup d'entre vous, je le devine, rechignent à écouter un conseiller aussi jeune. Pourtant, rappelez-vous ! Lorsqu'un Addrak a tenté d'enlever le roi, lors de son jubilé, il y a quelques mois, c'est ce garçon qui a rassemblé vos dragons affolés ; c'est grâce à lui que vous avez pu chasser le sorcier et son horrible créature de fumée !

– C'est surtout grâce à Nour, corrige Cham. Sans lui…

Messire Onys sourit :

– Tu as raison, petit. D'ailleurs, que serait un dragonnier sans son dragon ?

Puis il annonce :

– J'ai réfléchi. Mieux qu'un discours, c'est une démonstration qu'il vous faut. Cham, Yénor va te prêter sa monture. Nous allons nous rendre à la plaine d'entraînement. Et tu vas nous montrer ce dont est capable un dragonnier qui communique avec son dragon.

Le garçon en reste bouche bée. Lui ? Il va chevaucher Nour ? Devant ces dragonniers expérimentés ?

Puis une bouffée de fierté lui gonfle la poitrine : oh, oui ! Il va le leur montrer !

L'heure qui suit passe comme un rêve, pour Cham. On le revêt d'une combinaison de cuir brune, semblable à celle que portent les dragonniers. Il se met en selle, fixe autour de ses chevilles et de sa poitrine les harnais de sécurité. Messire Onys lui donne un court poignard que le garçon passe à sa ceinture. Il lui servira à trancher les lanières des harnais, au cas où il lui faudrait s'en libérer d'urgence. D'un cri, Cham encourage Nour :

– On décolle !

Et ils s'envolent.

C'est alors un enchaînement d'acrobaties plus hardies les unes que les autres : pirouettes, descentes en vrille, remontées à la verticale, virages sur l'aile, glissades tête en bas, accélérations foudroyantes… Jamais le garçon ne s'est autant amusé !

«Tu te souviens de notre premier vol ?» demande-t-il en pensée.

«Tu étais bien lourd, alors, pour le dragonneau que j'étais ! répond Nour, amusé. Aujourd'hui, tu ne pèses pas plus qu'une plume !»

Soudain, une idée folle vient à l'esprit de Cham. Il la propose à sa monture. Celle-ci pique aussitôt vers le sol à la vitesse de l'éclair. En bas, les dragonniers poussent un cri d'effroi, croyant les voir s'écraser. À la dernière seconde, le dragon se redresse, freine de toute la largeur de ses ailes et se pose sans même déranger un caillou.

Alors Cham, rayonnant, lance :

— Messire Onys ! Si on organisait une fausse bataille ? Je serais un Addrak, et les dragonniers me poursuivraient. Nour et moi, on s'efforcerait de leur échapper.

— Quoi ? lâche le Maître Dragonnier. Vingt-six hommes contre toi ?

Puis, avec un large sourire, il approuve :

— Excellent exercice, Cham ! Allez tous seller vos dragons !

Le soir venu, messire Onys fait au roi Bertram et aux magiciennes le récit de ce stupéfiant après-midi.

— C'était tout simplement fabuleux, conclut-il. Cham a démontré qu'une parfaite entente entre un dragonnier et son dragon permet des exploits inimaginables.

— Et il a échappé à ses poursuivants ? s'émerveille le roi.

— Non seulement il ne s'est pas laissé attraper, mais il a réussi à leur arracher à chacun, grâce à son poignard, une ceinture ou un lambeau de vêtement. Sans en blesser aucun ! Imaginez ce dont ce garçon sera capable quand il saura manier l'épée !

Le souverain acquiesce :

— Oui, il sera un combattant redoutable. Le digne successeur de messire Damian… En plus de ses leçons de magie, il est temps de

l'instruire dans l'art du combat. Nous avons grand besoin d'un dragonnier comme lui.

– Pour être dragonnier, commence Isendrine, il faut…

– … avoir un dragon, termine Mélisande.

– En effet, belles dames, soupire messire Onys. Or, de nouveaux dragonneaux ne devraient pas naître sur l'île aux Dragons avant huit bonnes années. C'est long…

Les magiciennes s'approchent de la fenêtre. Elles observent un instant le ciel où monte une lune presque ronde. Puis leur regard se perd vers l'horizon, que la nuit obscurcit. Alors, elles chantonnent :

– Quand un dragon a déjà un nom…

– … pourquoi ne naîtrait-il pas hors saison ?

– Que voulez-vous dire ? s'étonne le roi.

Les dames aux cheveux rouges chantonnent encore, énigmatiques :

– Qui connaît les pensées des dragons ? Leur âme…

– … est un mystère, Sire. Un grand mystère.

9

La magie des élusims

Le lendemain matin, lorsque Nyne sort dans la cour, un tiède rayon de soleil lui caresse le visage. Entendant le pas de sa mère derrière elle, elle s'écrie :

– Quelle belle journée, hein, maman !

Dhydra entoure de son bras les épaules de la fillette :

– Oui, le printemps est là. L'air avait la même douceur il y a onze ans, je m'en souviens. Le matin où ton frère est né.

– Oh ! lâche la petite fille. C'est son anniversaire ? Aujourd'hui ?

– Pas aujourd'hui, non… Dans trois jours.

Elle a dit ça sur un ton si étrange que Nyne lève vers elle un regard interrogateur.

Sa mère ajoute, pensive :

– Et la nuit d'avant, ce sera la nouvelle lune.

Nyne se souvient alors du récit que Dhydra leur a fait : la pierre de Semblance, le sortilège lancé sur les Addraks n'aura plus d'effet.

D'une voix un peu tremblante, elle demande :

– Les sorciers vont redevenir… normaux, c'est ça ?

Sa mère acquiesce de la tête.

Soudain, la petite fille fronce les sourcils :

– C'est bizarre… Juste quand Cham aura ses onze ans…

– Oui, juste ce jour-là ! À l'heure où l'aube effacera la nuit, l'heure où Cham a poussé son premier cri. La course des astres nous apporte le meilleur comme le pire.

Dhydra ajoute avec un sourire :

– Mais elle nous offre aussi de jolies surprises. Voilà longtemps, il me semble, que tu ne t'es pas promenée sur la plage…

– Sur la plage ? répète la fillette, intriguée.

Elle tourne les yeux vers le chemin qui mène à la falaise. Depuis le bord, un sentier très raide descend jusqu'au rivage. C'est là, sept mois plus tôt, qu'elle a ramassé dans les galets l'œuf bleuté qui contenait un curieux animal…

– Vag, souffle-t-elle. Mon ami Vag…

Depuis que l'élusim l'a transportée jusqu'à la Citadelle Noire pour qu'elle apporte le miroir à sa mère, elle ne l'a pas revu. Vag est-il de retour ? A-t-il quelque chose à lui dire ?

Pleine d'espoir, elle s'exclame :

– Je peux y aller tout de suite, maman ? Je donnerai leur grain aux poules après, promis !

– Va, Nyne ! Aujourd'hui, c'est moi qui m'occuperai des volailles. Va vite !

Elle regarde, amusée, la fillette partir à toutes jambes.

«Tu m'as rendu mon miroir, petite magicienne, songe-t-elle. Il faut bien que tu aies un objet à toi, à présent. Un objet chargé de magie. Et la magie des élusims est une belle magie…»

Tout en dévalant le sentier, Nyne se rappelle la curieuse impression qu'elle a ressentie, le matin où Cham s'est envolé vers Nalsara. Il lui a semblé entendre dans le grondement des vagues de mystérieuses paroles. Étaient-ce les élusims qui discutaient entre eux, là-bas, dans leur lointain royaume marin? Et si, bientôt, ils avaient besoin d'elle?

Maintenant, elle en est sûre, Vag va apparaître. Il lui apporte sans doute un message. Peut-être a-t-il même une mission à lui confier? À cette idée, elle a le cœur qui bat d'excitation:

«Cham va être dragonnier, et moi magicienne. Je le suis déjà, maman l'a dit. Je suis capable de défendre Ombrune, comme mon frère.»

La voilà en bas de la falaise. Essoufflée,

les joues rougies, elle court jusqu'à la ligne humide où les vagues viennent mourir sur les galets, et elle fixe la mer. Elle ne voit que les rouleaux d'eau sombre qui déferlent l'un après l'autre dans un jaillissement d'écume blanche. Elle attend, impatiente. Les minutes s'égrènent, et rien ne se passe. Pourquoi sa mère l'a-t-elle envoyée sur la plage si ce n'est pas pour y retrouver Vag ? Il est vrai que Dhydra n'a pas parlé de l'élusim. C'est elle, Nyne, qui s'est imaginé…

Un tourbillon de vent lui plaque les cheveux sur la figure, et la petite fille les écarte de la main, agacée. Les embruns mouillent sa robe, elle commence à avoir froid. Elle aurait dû mettre sa pèlerine…

À cet instant, elle écarquille les yeux. Car, d'une vague plus grosse que les autres émerge une tête grise au bout d'un long cou, puis un large dos ruisselant.

– Vag !

Le chantonnement familier résonne à ses oreilles :

– Hrummm ! Hrumm, hrummmm…

– Vag ! Je suis si contente de te voir ! Maman m'a envoyée sur la plage. Tu l'avais prévenue que tu venais ?

La voix de l'élusim résonne dans la tête de Nyne :

« Oh, elle l'a deviné, et aussi que je t'apportais un cadeau. »

– Un cadeau ? se réjouit la fillette. Un cadeau… magique ?

« Tu t'intéresses à la magie, petite Nyne ? »

– Je suis magicienne, tu sais. Comme maman.

Elle a déclaré ça avec tant de sérieux et de fierté que l'élusim penche la tête, un peu taquin :

«Oh, vraiment? En ce cas, ceci te sera utile. Tiens, prends!»

Nyne tend la main. Et Vag, approchant son museau, dépose dans la paume ouverte un objet scintillant:

«La nacre dont est fait cet anneau provient d'un coquillage très rare, appelé "oreille de mer". Il a le don d'entendre les souhaits silencieux de celui ou de celle qui le porte. Du moins, si cette personne possède certains pouvoirs...»

Nyne contemple l'anneau avec émotion. Il est tout simple. Pourtant, il est magique!

«Passe-le à ton doigt!» l'encourage l'élusim.

La fillette obéit. Et aussitôt, elle formule une demande dans sa tête:

«Anneau, montre-moi mon frère!»

Elle ferme les yeux, s'attendant à voir des images. Mais derrière ses paupières n'apparaissent que des taches grises et blanches, couleur des vagues.

«Hrumm! Hrumm, hrumm, hrumm...! rit l'élusim. La magie ne fonctionne pas n'importe quand ni pour n'importe quoi, voyons ! »

— Je n'ai pas souhaité n'importe quoi, grogne Nyne, un peu vexée.

Vag balance gentiment la tête :

« Rappelle-toi le miroir, le cristal-qui-voit, *Le Livre des Secrets* ! Répondaient-ils à toutes vos questions ? »

— Non, reconnaît la fillette. Seulement quand on en avait besoin.

« Eh bien, l'anneau fait de même. S'il faut que tu saches quelque chose, il te préviendra. »

— Il me… parlera ?

« À sa façon. C'est ton doigt qui te le dira. Je dois te laisser, à présent, petite Nyne. Surtout, ne perds pas ton anneau et ne le donne à personne ! Il n'appartient qu'à toi. »

— Attends !

L'élusim a déjà plongé. Son dos gris émerge encore un instant à la surface, avant de disparaître. Il est parti.

— Oh, Vag ! Je n'ai même pas eu le temps de te demander quand je te reverrai, marmonne Nyne, attristée.

Levant la main, elle contemple l'anneau de nacre qui luit doucement.

— C'est mon doigt qui me le dira, soupire-t-elle. Si j'ai vraiment besoin de le savoir…

Décidément, la magie n'est pas toujours si magique que ça !

Tout le reste de la journée, Nyne ne cesse de regarder sa main, de faire tourner l'anneau autour de son doigt. Elle a bien envie de l'interroger de nouveau. Elle aimerait tant avoir des nouvelles de son frère, apprendre à quoi ressemble sa vie d'écuyer à la Dragonnerie royale ! Mais elle n'ose pas poser ses questions. Si elle n'obtenait pas de réponse, elle serait trop déçue.

Après le souper, quand Nyne monte dans sa chambre, elle va se poster un instant devant la fenêtre ouverte et lève les yeux vers la lune. Elle sera bientôt pleine. Les sorciers addraks seront libérés du sortilège de pétrification. La petite fille revoit l'imposante Citadelle Noire, telle qu'elle lui est apparue quand elle a rapporté le miroir à sa mère sur le dos de Vag. C'est en captant un rayon de lune avec le miroir qu'elle a pu prévenir Dhydra de sa présence. La lune l'a aidée, cette nuit-là. Dans trois nuits, ce sont les Addraks qui profiteront de sa lumière.

À mi-voix, elle médite :

— La lune n'est ni bonne ni mauvaise. Elle suit sa course dans le ciel, voilà tout.

Le lendemain, Nyne est réveillée juste avant l'aube par un curieux picotement à son doigt. D'un geste machinal, elle tourne un peu l'anneau. Le picotement ne cesse pas. Au contraire, il s'accentue.

Dans la pénombre, Nyne fixe l'objet de nacre, perplexe :

– Tu veux me dire quelque chose ?

Va-t-elle avoir une vision ? Des mots vont-ils retentir dans sa tête ?

Non, elle ne voit rien, elle n'entend rien. Pourtant, elle éprouve le besoin impérieux de se lever, d'aller à la fenêtre.

Elle ouvre la croisée, se penche au-dehors.

Selka ! La petite fille reconnaît aussitôt la belle créature aux écailles d'émeraude.

La dragonne s'éloigne à lents battements d'ailes. Bientôt, elle s'enfonce entre les nuages et disparaît.

– Selka…, souffle Nyne. Tu es venue dans l'île. Pourquoi ?

Un nouveau picotement à son doigt l'oblige à fermer les yeux. Alors, elle *voit*. Sur l'écran de ses paupières closes, une image se forme. Celle de ce rocher qui surplombe la mer, à l'ouest, et ressemble à un chien couché. Entre les pattes du « chien » repose une chose ovale, beige, piquetée de taches brunes.

En trois bonds, Nyne est à la porte de sa chambre. Elle dévale l'escalier en criant :

– Papa ! Maman ! Il y a un œuf dans l'île ! Un œuf de dragon !

Le présent de Selka

Au petit matin, Cham pénètre dans le box de Nour avec un seau d'eau fraîche. Le dragon tourne vers lui son regard doré :

« C'est un grand jour pour toi, petit maître. »

– Pourquoi tu dis ça ? Tu te trompes, c'est après-demain que j'aurai mes onze ans !

« Oui, oui… Mais n'as-tu rien ressenti de particulier, en te réveillant ? »

Cham verse dans l'abreuvoir le contenu de son seau. La question du dragon fait remonter en lui un vague souvenir : en s'éveillant, il lui a semblé que, derrière la fenêtre, deux yeux le fixaient. Des yeux d'une couleur inhabituelle, d'un blanc laiteux, où brillaient deux pupilles d'argent.

Il secoue la tête. Allons, c'est idiot ! Ce n'était qu'un reflet sur les carreaux.

Avec un gloussement, il répond :

— Tu sais, au saut du lit, les humains n'ont pas toujours les idées très claires !

La voix mentale du dragon se fait insistante :

« Cham ! Si tu veux progresser dans la pratique de la magie, tu dois apprendre à faire confiance à tes visions, même les plus fugitives ! Dis-moi, qu'as-tu *vu* ? »

Troublé, le garçon hésite :

— J'ai cru voir… J'ai vu… des yeux pas ordinaires. Tout blancs.

« Des yeux aveugles ? »

— Oh non, pas aveugles ! Des yeux qui voyaient… autrement.

Un long frisson fait cliqueter les écailles de Nour :

« D'après une très ancienne légende, le premier des dragons avait ces yeux-là. Depuis des siècles et des siècles, nous attendons que naisse un dragon qui lui ressemble. Un dragon blanc… »

– Un dragon blanc ? souffle Cham. Il y a quelques jours, dans un rêve éveillé, j'ai chevauché un dragon blanc. Mon dragon. Je l'ai appelé Cyd.

« Tu as bien choisi son nom, approuve Nour. Il signifie "Lumière". »

– Ah… ?

Machinalement, le garçon s'empare d'une brosse, soulève une des pattes de Nour et lui astique les griffes, sans un mot, les sourcils froncés. Le dragon respecte son silence.

Enfin, Cham reprend :

– D'après Isendrine et Mélisande, c'était une image de mon avenir. Un avenir proche… Crois-tu que Cyd va naître sur l'île aux Dragons ? Crois-tu qu'il est déjà éclos ?

Tendant son autre patte, Nour répond :

« Éclos ? Hmmmm… sûrement pas. Mais

n'ai-je pas dit que c'était un grand jour pour toi, petit maître ? »

Comme Cham reste la brosse en l'air, le dragon ajoute d'un ton presque taquin :

« Laisse mes griffes, elles brillent assez comme ça ! Et va donc interroger cette boule de verre que tu gardes dans ta chambre ! Voilà bien longtemps, il me semble, que tu ne l'as pas sortie de son coffret. »

Le cristal-qui-voit ! Bien sûr ! Le cristal-qui-voit lui révélera tout !

– J'y vais ! s'exclame le garçon.

Et, sans se demander comment Nour connaît l'existence de la boule magique, il traverse en courant la cour de la dragon-nerie, franchit une porte, grimpe un escalier quatre à quatre et surgit, essoufflé, dans sa petite chambre sous le toit.

Il s'accroupit, pose devant lui le coffret de plomb et ordonne :

– *Effractet !*

Le couvercle se soulève. Cham prend entre ses mains le cristal scintillant. Aussitôt, il est emporté par un grand souffle de vent.

Le voilà au-dessus de l'île aux Dragons. Il reconnaît les rochers découpés de la côte ouest. Celui-ci, surtout, qui ressemble à un chien couché. Un étroit sentier y descend. Sur le sentier, trois silhouettes viennent d'apparaître. La plus petite gambade devant. C'est Nyne ! Elle désigne quelque chose, joyeuse, les cheveux au vent. Puis elle se penche, prend entre ses bras un objet ovale, beige, piqueté de taches brunes. Un œuf de dragon !

Une nuée lumineuse passe alors devant les yeux de Cham. Puis une tête apparaît, couverte d'écailles vertes aux reflets émeraude. Selka!

La voix de la dragonne résonne à l'intérieur de son crâne :

«Je te fais cadeau de ton dragon, Cham, ainsi que je l'ai promis à messire Damian. Aucun dragonnier n'en aura jamais chevauché de semblable. Et tu lui as donné le plus beau des noms : Cyd! Lumière!»

La vision s'efface. Cham se retrouve à genoux sur le plancher, une simple boule de verre entre les mains.

— Je vais avoir un dragon, murmure-t-il. Je vais avoir *mon* dragon…

Une bouffée de bonheur l'envahit : s'il possède un dragon, alors… il est dragonnier!

À peine a-t-il eu cette pensée que la pièce s'obscurcit. Dehors, le ciel est devenu noir. Une brume ténébreuse se colle aux carreaux. Cham frissonne : qu'il fait froid, soudain! Une peur glacée s'insinue dans ses veines tandis qu'une pensée sans mots rampe dans son cerveau. C'est une pensée de haine, mêlée à un ricanement silencieux. La strige se moque de lui. Elle le défie. La créature lui semble plus redoutable que jamais, plus chargée encore de force maléfique. Bientôt, son maître et les onze autres sorciers retrouveront la liberté.

Le garçon prend soudain conscience d'une chose terrible: le sortilège de pétrification qui immobilise les Addraks cessera le jour de son anniversaire! Plus que deux nuits…

Mais le soleil matinal éclaire de nouveau la chambre. Sans doute Cham est-il le seul à avoir perçu l'effrayant phénomène. Avec Nour et les magiciennes.

Saisi d'angoisse, il implore en lui-même:
« Cyd! Oh, Cyd, dépêche-toi d'éclore! Contre toute cette noirceur, je vais avoir grand besoin de lumière! »

Dans son antre, la strige tremble encore de fureur. Un dragon va naître, elle le sait, elle le sent. Un dragon différent des autres.

Ce qu'il y a de plus noir en elle palpite fiévreusement. Car le dragon et le garçon qu'elle hait sont liés. Ça aussi, elle le sait. Pour le moment, elle domine le garçon. Elle reste capable de l'effrayer. Le pourra-t-elle encore lorsqu'il chevauchera le dragon? Avec l'aide du sorcier, son maître, peut-être... Son maître la rejoindra prochainement, empli d'une puissance nouvelle.

Cependant, pour la première fois, la créature éprouve quelque chose qui ressemble à de la peur. Elle n'aime pas ça.

Prenant la forme d'une boule dure, d'un gris de cendre, elle se heurte avec violence aux parois de son antre, rebondit sur le roc. Si elle pouvait *sortir*... La magie qui la soumet à son maître l'en empêche, et elle enrage. Si elle pouvait sortir, elle irait détruire l'œuf maudit. Car il contient ce qu'elle ne supporte pas : une pure blancheur.

Antos et Dhydra ont suivi leur fille jusqu'au rocher du Chien. En effet, il y a un œuf, là, bien calé entre de grosses pierres.

— Un œuf de dragon ! s'exclame le Grand Éleveur, stupéfait. À cette saison ! Pas même un an après les dernières éclosions !

— C'est le dragon de Cham, papa, déclare Nyne.

Soulevant doucement l'œuf dans ses bras, elle reprend :

— C'est le dragon de Cham, hein, maman ? C'est pour ça qu'il est spécial !

Dhydra approuve de la tête.

Antos, lui, est tout désorienté :

— D'habitude, on laisse les œufs au soleil. Puis, au bout de quarante jours, on les porte à l'abri dans la grange, mais celui-ci...

Il interroge sa femme du regard.

— Oui, dit-elle, celui-ci est différent. C'est le cadeau de Selka à un futur jeune dragonnier pour son anniversaire.

— Son anniversaire ? C'est dans deux jours...

Dhydra fixe l'horizon, la mine grave :

— Bien des choses s'accompliront, dans deux jours : les sorciers addraks retrouveront leur corps de chair, Cham aura onze ans, et un dragon naîtra. Un dragon semblable à celui de la légende, semblable au premier des dragons.

— Comment tu le sais, maman? demande Nyne.

— Je l'ai vu en rêve. Ton frère aussi l'a vu.

Un sourire éclaire alors le visage de la jeune femme :

— Allons! Portons vite cet œuf dans la grange! Qu'il reste bien au chaud dans la paille jusqu'à son éclosion!

Enjouée, elle se tourne vers son mari :

— Vous n'aurez jamais eu un aussi beau dragonneau à soigner, Grand Éleveur!

11

La dernière nuit

Un jour est passé, puis une nuit, un autre jour encore. Un nouveau soir descend sur Ombrune, sur le Territoire des Addraks. La lune, dans le ciel, dessine un cercle parfait.

Dans sa chambre-grotte, au cœur des Mornes Monts, Nastrad, le vieux chaman, est assis sur sa natte de jonc. Un bruit léger lui fait tourner la tête :

— C'est toi, Igrid ? Tu ne dors pas ?

La rouquine vient se blottir contre lui :

— C'est à l'aube que les effets de la pierre

de Semblance prendront fin, grand-père. Les Addraks…

Sa voix a tremblé, elle s'interrompt. Le vieil homme termine à sa place :

— Oui, demain matin, à l'instant où les premières lueurs du jour feront pâlir la pleine lune, ils seront libérés.

— Et si tu trouvais un moyen de… prolonger le sortilège ?

— Malheureusement, c'est impossible.

— Ils garderont tout de même chacun une main ou un pied de pierre. Tu crois que ça va beaucoup les gêner ?

— Hmmm… Pas très commode pour courir ou pour manier l'épée, non ?

Ils pouffent tous les deux. En vérité, Nastrad dissimule son inquiétude. Car, il en est sûr, les Addraks découvriront sûrement bientôt l'existence du Libre Peuple. Les gens de la tribu ne sont pas des guerriers. Ils sont forts et agiles ; ils connaissent tous les secrets de la montagne et, s'ils doivent combattre, le chaman les soutiendra avec ses sortilèges. Cela suffira-t-il, face à la magie noire ?

Cependant, depuis quelque temps, le vieil aveugle fait chaque nuit le même rêve, qui le laisse au réveil empli d'espérance et de joie. Dans ce rêve, il se trouve au sommet des Mornes Monts, et il *voit* la neige du glacier scintiller à la lumière de la lune. Alors, une grande ombre passe au-dessus de lui. Il lève les yeux. Un dragon traverse le ciel, filant vers les plaines du Nord. Un magnifique dragon blanc.

Pressant la main d'Igrid, il murmure :

– Aie confiance, fillette. Ces sinistres personnages finiront par être vaincus.

– Peut-être, grand-père. Mais, cette nuit, je ne pourrai pas dormir...

Dans la salle secrète des sorciers, à la lueur lugubre des torches magiques, rien ne bouge. Les douze statues attendent toujours, figées dans leur dernier geste, leur dernier cri.

Emprisonné par sa gangue de pierre, l'esprit de Darkat est engourdi. Et voilà que, pour la première fois depuis des jours et des nuits, sa conscience frémit : il a perçu

un appel. Il vibrait de tant de haine qu'il a pénétré la pierre, s'est enfoncé jusqu'au cœur du sorcier. Ce cœur qui n'a pas cessé de battre dans son corps pétrifié. Ce cœur qui bat un peu plus vite en recevant l'appel sans mots. Car il provient de la strige. Il parle de détruire. Tout de suite, il y a urgence. La strige veut agir. Elle veut sortir. Et elle ne le peut pas sans l'ordre de son maître.

Les pensées de Darkat se débattent, prisonnières, comme la strige est prisonnière entre les parois de son antre. La malédiction qui le tient captif est sur le point de céder, il le pressent. Mais le moment n'est pas encore venu. Lorsqu'il viendra, ce sera trop tard. Un danger menace, fait de blancheur, de lumière insoutenable.

Dans sa poitrine de pierre, le cœur vivant du sorcier palpite à en exploser. Il doit ordonner à la strige de partir. Maintenant. Or, il est muet, paralysé. Il lutte désespérément pour retrouver un minuscule espace de liberté. Combien de temps dure ce combat silencieux ? Le sorcier l'ignore. Il ignore aussi qu'au-dehors les heures du jour ont passé une à une, que la nuit est venue. Pourtant, quelque chose en lui le sait. Quand le crépuscule étend son ombre sur la Terre, un frisson de noirceur se faufile par la fêlure de la pierre provoquée par l'appel de la strige. Cela lui donne la force de formuler un mot, un seul :

– Va !

La strige n'en attendait pas davantage. Elle est libre !

Prenant la forme qu'elle préfère, celle d'un énorme dragon de fumée, la créature

133

s'élance hors de son antre. Dans la nuit tombée, elle plane un instant au-dessus de la Citadelle Noire. Puis elle file vers Ombrune, vers ceux qu'elle hait, vers la chose détestable qu'elle veut détruire.

À Nalsara, Isendrine et Mélisande observent leur cuve de mercure, où se forment d'inquiétantes ondulations. Des vapeurs s'en élèvent, d'une vilaine teinte verdâtre. Elles montent vers le plafond voûté, dessinent des boucles dans les airs. Les magiciennes déchiffrent à mi-voix cette écriture énigmatique :

– Haine et rage…

– … engendrent mort et carnage.

La guerre, encore. Depuis quelque temps, les présages ne disent que ça. Cette fois, cependant, le métal liquide clapote bizarrement, comme s'il peinait à composer les signes magiques.

Les dames aux cheveux rouges passent les mains au-dessus de la cuve, mêlant leurs longs doigts aux fumerolles vertes :

– Parle ! Ne crains pas…

– … de voir et de nommer ce que tu vois !

Les vapeurs se dissipent, le mercure s'apaise un instant. Puis il lance un jet de gouttelettes, qui décrivent des arabesques argentées avant de retomber dans la cuve.

Les magiciennes lâchent une exclamation :

– L'œuf de dragon…

– … est en danger !

Passant par la fente des rideaux, un rayon de lune vient caresser la joue de Dhydra, endormie. Elle ouvre les yeux. Ce n'est pourtant pas cette faible lueur qui l'a tirée du sommeil ; non, c'est un brusque sentiment d'angoisse, qui lui dessèche la bouche.

– Mon miroir…, souffle-t-elle.

L'objet magique est près d'elle, sur la table de nuit. Elle tend la main pour le prendre, jette un coup d'œil à la surface de verre. Alors, elle retient un cri d'effroi. La strige! La strige vole vers l'île! La magicienne comprend aussitôt: la créature vient détruire l'œuf.

Sans bruit, pour ne pas réveiller Antos, Dhydra se lève. À l'instant de quitter la chambre, elle lance à mi-voix en direction de son époux:

– *Snotva, wanna-to !* Dors, je le veux!

Elle jette en hâte une pèlerine sur son dos, sort de la maison et court vers la grange.

Lorsqu'elle pousse la porte, la lumière de la lune vient se poser sur l'œuf, dans son nid de paille.

Debout sur le seuil, la magicienne le contemple, anxieuse: saura-t-elle protéger le dragon?

Elle se retourne, observe le ciel. Pour l'instant, aucune ombre ne trouble la nuit claire. L'île baigne dans un silence bleuté. Pourtant, le miroir ne peut pas se tromper.

La strige va surgir. Qui l'envoie? Les sorciers resteront pétrifiés jusqu'à l'aube. La créature a-t-elle échappé à son maître? À moins que…

«Darkat, comprend Dhydra. Es-tu en train de devenir aussi puissant que notre père Eddhor? As-tu réussi à lancer la strige sur nous malgré le sortilège qui te rend immobile et muet?»

Ironique, elle ajoute entre ses dents:

— As-tu donc si peur de ce dragon qui va naître, mon frère?

À cet instant, un crissement de gravier l'alerte: une silhouette encapuchonnée vient de surgir.

— Nyne! souffle la jeune femme. Que fais-tu ici?

— Et toi, maman? rétorque la fillette.

Dhydra en reste coite. Nyne explique:

— Mon anneau m'a réveillée, il me brûlait le doigt. J'ai compris ce qu'il m'annonçait à sa manière: la strige arrive, hein? Elle vient briser l'œuf?

Plus bas, elle poursuit:

– Seulement, l'anneau ne m'a pas dit ce qu'il fallait faire. J'ai peur, maman…

Dhydra prend entre ses mains le mince visage anxieux tendu vers elle :

– Tu as peur, et c'est bien naturel. Pourtant, tu es venue. Et nous allons combattre la strige ensemble, petite magicienne. D'ailleurs, la voilà…

En effet, une ombre gigantesque vient d'obscurcir le ciel. La lune disparaît ; la nuit est si noire, tout à coup, que c'est à peine si Nyne distingue encore sa mère, à côté d'elle. Une rafale glacée fait voltiger les pans de leurs pèlerines et manque de les jeter à terre. Elles se raccrochent l'une à l'autre.

Dhydra doit crier pour se faire entendre dans les mugissements du vent :

– Lève la main, Nyne ! Sers-toi du pouvoir de l'anneau ! Ordonne à la strige de reculer !

La fillette obéit. À la terreur qui monte en elle se mêle une force qu'elle ne connaissait pas.

Deux mots lui viennent à la bouche. Elle ne sait pas ce qu'ils signifient, mais elle a entendu Cham les hurler la première fois qu'il a combattu la strige, au palais royal, lors des fêtes du jubilé :

– *Horlor gorom !*

Elle n'est pas étonnée d'entendre sa mère lancer elle aussi ces mêmes mots. Ensemble, elles les répètent encore et encore, jusqu'à en avoir la gorge en feu.

Hélas ! ils ne produisent aucun effet. La tempête maléfique redouble de violence. Des éclairs dessinent des fourches blêmes qui illuminent les ténèbres. Le vent secoue la grange, les murs tremblent, les poutres grincent, des tuiles s'envolent. Si le bâtiment s'écroule, Dhydra et Nyne seront ensevelies sous les décombres, l'œuf sera brisé, le dragon ne naîtra jamais...

Cependant, la grange résiste. Nyne perçoit autour d'elle la vibration d'énergie magique émise par sa mère : Dhydra lutte avec un courage incroyable !

Soudain, un craquement effrayant retentit : l'une des grosses poutres du toit s'est fendue. La petite fille s'affole :

— On n'y arrivera pas, maman ! On n'est pas assez fortes !

— On y arrivera, Nyne ! réplique sa mère. Tiens bon ! Nous ne sommes plus seules !

Et Nyne voit apparaître deux licornes ailées, d'une blancheur éclatante, qui galopent sur le noir des nuées :

— Isendrine et Mélisande ! Ce sont elles ! Ce sont les magiciennes !

12

La lumière de l'aube

Cham s'agite dans son sommeil. Il se hâte en rêve sur un sentier qui domine la mer. Des nuages d'orage roulent au-dessus de lui, et le garçon a peur : l'œuf est en danger.

Un éclair jaillit, frappe le rocher du Chien. Un gros éclat de pierre tombe sur la coquille beige, qui se brise.

– NON !

Cham se dresse sur son lit, en sueur. Quel affreux cauchemar !

Une rafale de vent secoue alors la fenêtre. Derrière les carreaux, la nuit est d'un noir d'encre. D'un bond, Cham est debout. Il a reconnu cette noirceur. Le rêve était un avertissement : la strige vient détruire l'œuf ! Elle veut empêcher l'éclosion du dragon blanc ! Le garçon doit se rendre sur l'île ! Sa mère va tout faire pour protéger l'œuf, bien sûr. Mais, seule, elle ne sera pas assez puissante.

Un instant, il pense courir jusqu'au box de Nour. Nour l'emmènerait sur son dos. Il renonce vite à cette idée : c'est à lui de défendre Cyd, son dragon. Il est capable de voler jusqu'à l'île, il lui suffit de se transformer en oiseau. Il l'a déjà fait.

Il ouvre la fenêtre, se prépare à prononcer la formule qui le changera en moineau.

Et il se ravise : il doit pouvoir traverser les nuées d'orage, fondre sur l'île comme une flèche. Un moineau n'est ni assez rapide ni assez costaud. Cette fois, il doit être… un aigle !

Cham a lu des noms d'oiseaux en langue des dragons dans le livre de magie. Aigle, c'était… *Kornil*. Non, *Kroniol*.

– *Kroniol !* lance-t-il.

Et il s'envole.

Les licornes sont passées à l'attaque. Elles enfoncent sans relâche leur corne scintillante, chargée d'énergie magique, dans la nuée ténébreuse. Mais celle-ci se défend. Prenant la forme d'un gigantesque dragon aux yeux jaunes, la strige étend vers les magiciennes deux pattes griffues. Des déchirures sanglantes apparaissent sur le pelage blanc des licornes. Nyne pousse un hurlement et lève le bras plus haut. L'anneau, à son doigt, jette des étincelles. L'une d'elles tourbillonne jusqu'à l'œil du monstre et s'y enfonce. La strige rugit de douleur, elle recule.

C'est alors qu'un étrange oiseau jaillit des ténèbres. Il a un long bec crochu, des serres puissantes. Son plumage est brun, mais ses ailes sont blanches, et sa queue est ornée de longues plumes de couleur.

Il se jette sur la créature, qui se replie sur elle-même. Un moment, on croirait que la

masse noirâtre a avalé l'oiseau, qu'elle l'a étouffé. Non, il ressort, s'élance de nouveau.

— Soutenons ton frère, Nyne ! crie Dhydra.

Quoi ? Ce drôle de volatile est son frère ? La petite fille s'en étonnera plus tard. Pour l'instant, elle reprend son imprécation avec plus de vigueur que jamais :

— *Horlor gorom !*

La strige revient à l'assaut. Une bourrasque d'une violence inouïe secoue la grange, qui craque de toutes parts. Des débris de tuiles tombent dans la paille. Affolée, Nyne se précipite vers l'œuf et le couvre de son corps. Il ne faut pas que la coquille soit brisée !

— Nyne ! l'appelle sa mère. Reste près de moi !

Dhydra commence à désespérer. Les efforts réunis de l'oiseau et des magiciennes, les trois grandes et la petite, ne viennent pas à bout du monstre.

Une large silhouette surgit alors, les ailes étendues. Ses écailles jettent des éclairs émeraude. Sa gueule vomit un jet de flammes, qui teinte le ciel noir de lueurs rougeoyantes. C'est Selka!

À coups de pattes, à coups de queue, la dragonne attaque à son tour.

Les enfants ont déjà assisté à un combat semblable, la première fois que la strige a tenté d'enlever Cham, sur l'île. Il leur avait semblé, alors, que même un dragon ne pouvait rien contre cette chose molle, sans forme, qui se creuse et se gonfle, étouffant les flammes. Mais, comme ce jour-là, Selka joint sa voix à celle des humains :

– *Horlor gorom !*

Le mystérieux commandement retentit au-dessus de l'île tel un grondement de tonnerre. Reprenant courage, les licornes chargent, l'oiseau se jette de nouveau, bec en avant, sur l'affreuse masse noire.

C'est fini, la strige renonce. En une seconde, elle prend l'aspect d'un long reptile, qui file en sifflant de dépit et se perd à l'horizon.

Lorsque Nyne lève les yeux, elle voit Selka planer encore un instant au-dessus du champ de bataille. Puis, dans un lent battement d'ailes, elle s'éloigne à son tour.

La petite fille a mal au bras à force de l'avoir tenu dressé, et son doigt la picote. L'anneau jette encore quelques étincelles, puis redevient un simple cercle de nacre.

– C'est bien, jeune magicienne, dit sa mère.

– Je n'ai pas fait grand-chose, proteste Nyne.

Deux ombres s'approchent alors. Les magiciennes ont retrouvé leur apparence humaine. Leurs robes sont déchirées, tachées de sang. Mais elles sont rayonnantes.

– Comme chacun de nous, tu as fait ce que tu devais faire, dit Isendrine. Voilà pourquoi…

– … nous sommes victorieux, conclut Mélisande.

Le curieux oiseau atterrit sur le seuil de la grange. Il avance maladroitement dans la paille et tend le cou vers l'œuf beige. Puis, d'un coup, il tourbillonne sur lui-même et redevient garçon.

– Cham! s'écrie Nyne. C'est bien toi!

Les magiciennes lâchent, amusées:

– Joli travail, jeune magicien! Tu as créé…

– … une nouvelle espèce de rapace très originale!

Cham s'agenouille devant l'œuf. Il a eu si peur et il ressent à présent une telle joie qu'il a presque envie de pleurer: son dragon est là, prêt à éclore!

– Cyd…, murmure-t-il.

Il lève des yeux brillants vers sa mère, sa sœur, les magiciennes:

– Merci! Oh, merci! Sans vous…

– Tu nous as bien soutenues dans ce combat, Cham, dit sa mère. Même si ton apparition était assez cocasse! Quelle formule as-tu employée pour te transformer?

– Je voulais être un aigle. Il me semblait que le mot était *Kroniol*. Mais…

Les trois femmes s'esclaffent.

– Pas de doute, fait Isendrine, le mélange…

– … est inattendu! termine Mélisande.

Et Dhydra explique :

— Tu as combiné plusieurs termes, Cham : *Oriol*, aigle ; *Onil*, mouette, et… *Krool*, qui signifie coq !

— C'est pour ça que tu avais une si belle queue, avec des plumes de toutes les couleurs, pouffe Nyne.

Le garçon est un peu vexé, mais il prend le parti d'en rire lui aussi.

— L'aube…

— … se lève, murmurent les magiciennes.

Tous se tournent vers la porte de la grange, restée grande ouverte. Une faible lueur teinte de rose les graviers de la cour.

Dhydra attire son fils contre elle :

— Joyeux anniversaire, Cham ! Il y a onze ans, à cette heure-ci, je t'ai tenu dans mes bras pour la première fois.

À peine a-t-elle achevé sa phrase qu'un léger craquement retentit.

— L'œuf ! lâche Nyne. Sa coquille se fend ! Il va éclore !

Instinctivement, la petite fille et les trois femmes reculent. Elles sortent à pas lents, laissant Cham assister seul à la naissance de son dragon.

Boum, boum, boum...

Des chocs sourds ébranlent les marches. Dans la Citadelle Noire, les sorciers sortent l'un derrière l'autre de leur salle secrète. Dès que la lumière de l'aube a fait pâlir celle de la pleine lune, ils ont été libérés du sortilège. La pierre de Semblance n'est plus qu'un bloc de rocher ordinaire.

Les douze Addraks gravissent lourdement l'escalier, rejoignent la salle du Conseil, où ils se réunissent. Chacun s'assied dans son fauteuil au dossier sculpté. Ils restent un moment silencieux, s'observant les uns les autres. Sept d'entre eux ont un pied de pierre, quatre une main de pierre. Un seul a conservé à la fois une main et un pied pétrifiés : Darkat.

Le plus vieux d'entre eux, dont le front est orné d'un bandeau d'argent, lui jette un regard furieux :

— Eh bien, Darkat ! Voilà où nous ont

menés tes belles idées! Dans les marécages résidaient, disais-tu, des «forces inconnues, chargées d'une énergie fantastique». Nous saurions les dompter en unissant nos douze talents en magie noire! Et nous voici désormais handicapés! Par ta faute!

Les autres approuvent d'un grognement irrité.

Le jeune sorcier ne se laisse pas impressionner:

— Grand Maître, ce handicap est aussi une force. Ne le sentez-vous pas? Ne sentez-vous pas l'incroyable réserve d'énergie magique accumulée dans votre pied? Une énergie puisée dans la pierre de Semblance, et que notre magie noire va multiplier par deux, par trois, peut-être même par dix!

Comme pour prouver ses dires, il se lève, brandissant sa main de pierre et faisant claquer sur le sol son pied de pierre.

L'un des sorciers grommelle:

— Et comment expliques-tu que tu en aies *plus que nous*?

Tous les yeux se fixent sur Darkat. Le

Grand Maître, surtout, le toise avec colère. Serait-il… jaloux ?

Le cœur de Darkat bat à grands coups dans sa poitrine. Oui, il a reçu plus d'énergie que les autres. Dans sa main gauche, dans son pied droit. N'est-il pas le fils d'Eddhor, qui fut un sorcier redoutable ? Il plonge son regard dans celui de l'homme au bandeau d'argent :

– Grand Maître, j'ignore pourquoi j'ai gardé un double handicap – ou plutôt une double force. Mais soyez sûr que je mettrai cette force au service des Addraks et de leur gloire, comme je l'ai toujours fait.

Baissant modestement les yeux, il ajoute :

– Et comme mon père Eddhor m'a enseigné à le faire.

En lui-même, cependant, il pense :

« Bientôt, Grand Maître, c'est moi qui siégerai sur votre fauteuil. Car je serai le plus puissant d'entre vous ! »

Étirant ses lèvres en un rictus mauvais, le vieux sorcier ironise :

– Eh bien, Darkat, nous allons avoir

besoin de ta force, en effet. Car tu sais comme nous ce que l'aube nous a apporté ?

Il exécute de la main un geste magique. La lumière des torches diminue. Et, dans la pénombre, un cercle de clarté se forme peu à peu. Au centre du cercle apparaît Cham, agenouillé devant un gros œuf beige piqueté de taches brunes. Des craquelures courent à sa surface. Soudain, la coquille éclate. Une tête écailleuse apparaît. Le dragonneau s'extirpe de sa prison de calcaire et s'ébroue.

Les sorciers lâchent une exclamation : c'est un dragon blanc ! Dans ses yeux couleur de lait, les pupilles lancent des éclats argentés.

– Cyd ! murmure le garçon. Tu es Cyd, Lumière ! Tu es né pour combattre le noir. Et nous le combattrons ensemble !

À ces mots, la vision s'efface. Les douze sorciers restent muets, dans la clarté sinistre des torches magiques.

Épilogue

Antos s'étire et bâille longuement. Il a dormi comme un loir. Constatant que Dhydra est déjà levée, il saute du lit. Il entend alors des voix dans la cuisine. Nyne est debout, elle aussi ? Il fait à peine jour…

Intrigué, il passe un pantalon et sort de la chambre. Sur le seuil, il reste stupéfait. Il y a là sa femme, sa fille et… les magiciennes du palais !

— Mesdames, les salue-t-il en se recoiffant hâtivement avec les doigts.

Dhydra s'avance vers lui et caresse d'un geste tendre sa joue piquante :

— Tu vas bien, mon époux ? Je me suis permis de lancer sur toi un léger sortilège de sommeil. Nous avons eu une nuit un peu… agitée.

— Agitée ? Comment cela ?

Antos trouve parfois ces histoires de magiciennes extrêmement agaçantes.

Mais Nyne lui saute au cou, rieuse :

— Oh, papa ! Le dragon est né ! On vient d'aller le voir. Il est beau, tout blanc ! Cham est avec lui dans la grange.

— Cham ? Cham est ici, lui aussi ?

Décidément, Antos n'y comprend plus rien. Isendrine et Mélisande interviennent alors :

— Asseyez-vous, Grand Éleveur. Nous allons…

— … vous faire le récit de cette nuit pas comme les autres.

Au cœur des Mornes Monts, deux silhouettes marchent dans une galerie taillée dans la roche. Igrid conduit Nastrad jusqu'à l'ouverture qui donne sur les marécages. Le chaman aveugle a désiré sentir sur son visage la fraîcheur de l'aube.

Lorsqu'ils arrivent à l'extérieur, Igrid aide le vieil homme à s'asseoir sur un rocher.

— Comment est le ciel, ce matin, fillette ?

— Rose, grand-père. Et la lune a disparu.

Elle se tait avant de reprendre, hésitante :

– Les sorciers ne sont plus pétrifiés, n'est-ce pas ?

– Non, ils ne le sont plus.

Il saisit à tâtons la main de sa petite-fille.

– N'aie pas peur, mon enfant, ajoute-t-il. J'ai vu une blancheur dans le noir de la nuit. Une blancheur ailée.

– Tu veux dire… un dragon ?

– Oui, fillette. Un dragon blanc. Le dragon de ton ami Cham.

Igrid se tait et songe, émue :

« Cham va tenir sa promesse, alors ! Il va devenir un grand dragonnier ! Et… je vais peut-être le revoir bientôt. »

Très loin de là, dans le Royaume des Dragons, Selka s'incline devant la tombe de messire Damian :

« Ton désir est accompli, maître. Cham a son dragon. Tu avais vu juste : tu as été le plus vieux des dragonniers. Il sera le plus jeune. »

Levant la tête vers le ciel qui s'éclaircit, Selka ajoute :

« De terribles combats les attendent, tous les deux. Mais nous, les dragons, serons à leurs côtés. Quoi qu'il arrive. »

Retrouve vite Cham et Nyne
dans la suite des aventures de

Les dragons de Nalsara

Tome 14
Le cimetière des dragons

Mas
Oyama's
CLASSIC
KARATE

Mas Oyama's
CLASSIC
KARATE

Sterling Publishing Co., Inc.
New York

Translated by Tomoko Murakami and Jeffrey Cousminer
Illustrations by Toshiaki Morishita
Photographs by Kodansha Ltd.

2   4   6   8   10   9   7   5   3   1

Published 2004 by Sterling Publishing Co., Inc.
387 Park Avenue South, New York, NY 10016
Originally published in Japan © 1975 by Kodansha Ltd., Tokyo
Previously published as *Mas Oyama's Complete Karate Course*
and as *Karate School*
English translation © 1978 by Sterling Publishing Co., Inc.
Distributed in Canada by Sterling Publishing
c/o Canadian Manda Group, One Atlantic Avenue, Suite 105
Toronto, Ontario, Canada M6K 3E7
Distributed in Great Britain by Chrysalis Books Group PLC
The Chrysalis Building, Bramley Road, London W10 6SP, England
Distributed in Australia by Capricorn Link (Australia) Pty. Ltd.
P.O. Box 704, Windsor, NSW 2756, Australia

Sterling ISBN 1-4027-1287-1

Contents

第一章
空手の沿革

Mas Oyama instructing a prince of the Jordanian royal family in the fine points of karate.

Foreword

Karate is currently enjoying wide popularity the world over. We encounter it frequently in books, films, and on television. There are few people who have not seen a demonstration of brick or wood breaking or a single bare-handed man defeat a host of armed opponents.

But karate is much more than this. It was developed over a thousand years ago, not only as a form of unarmed combat, but as a way to discipline the body in order to improve the spirit. In this way, a unity of body and spirit could be achieved.

If this sounds too abstract, perhaps we can use terms that are easier to deal with. Besides conditioning the body and improving speed, strength, and co-ordination, karate increases one's alertness and self-awareness. It also teaches confidence— not cockiness or brashness—but a deep confidence in one's abilities to deal with the world around him. And with confidence comes calmness and a sense of inner peace.

This is the true karate, the karate that one can practice years after he can no longer break bricks. But everything must have a beginning and great things cannot be accomplished in a handful of days. In karate, the beginning is the physical forms—the punches, kicks, and blocks that we have all seen. These are the techniques that enable an adept kareteka to perform the seemingly impossible feats that he does.

Not everyone who studies karate achieves success, but if you are able to master the techniques described in this book, you could be one of them. Work with patience and perseverance and you are sure to find some measure of satisfaction. You must also work with caution, always bearing in mind that karate is a combat form and enables one to deliver a blow of devastating power. Techniques applied improperly or with insufficient care could cause injury to you or others.

May your pursuit of karate be a rewarding one.

1. Fundamentals of Karate

第二章
空手の基礎

THE HAND AND ARM AS WEAPONS

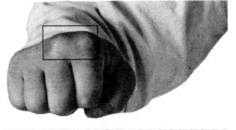

1. Seiken (normal fist)

This is the strongest and the most effective of the fist positions. *Seiken* is used when performing *Jodan-tsuki* (upper body thrust), a common position for attacking the face and the jaw; *Chudan-tsuki* (middle body thrust), the attack position for the chest and the stomach; and *Gedan-tsuki* (lower body thrust), for attacking the lower abdomen and groin. This fist can be used in defense as well as in attack.

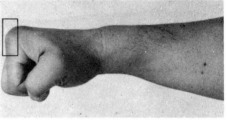

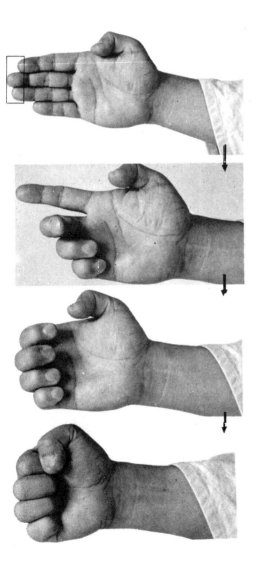

As shown in the first four photos, starting with the little finger, bend all four fingers so that their tips are digging tightly into the hand as close to their bases as possible. Bend the thumb over the second joints of the first two fingers to further tighten the fist.

When thrusting with the *Seiken,* you should strike the object directly with the knuckles of the first two fingers. In this position, if you strike an object with any of the other finger joints, you will most probably injure your hand. A punch with the fist in the *Seiken* position should be thrust straight out from the shoulder.

In the correct starting position, you should hold the fist with the palm facing up, touching your side on a level with your chest. Then, simultaneously, as you thrust forward, turn the fist inward so that at the point of attack the object will be struck by the knuckles of the first two fingers (in the final position, the palm should now be facing down). It is of utmost importance that at this point the arm and the back of the hand are held rigidly in a straight line, and that the object is being struck foremost by the knuckles of the first two fingers.

For beginners, the *Seiken* position is recommended for practice-sparring in order to avoid serious injuries while at the same time expressing great power.

A. *Seiken-chudan-tsuki* (middle body thrust with normal fist)

Starting with the fist in the normal position (the fist is held with the palm up, against the side and on a level with the chest), thrust forward in a straight line. At the point of striking the target, all the forward momentum should be transferred into the fist which is now held with the palm down. If there is any bend in the arm at this point, the transfer

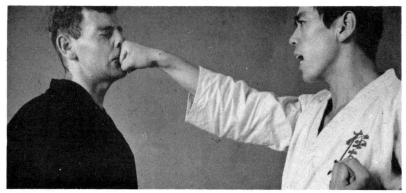

of power to the fist is inefficient. Further, it is probable that a wrist injury will result. It is obvious therefore, that you must time your punch so that it strikes the target a fraction of a second before the arm has reached its full extension in order for all its power to be spent on the target.

B. *Seiken-jodan-tsuki* (upper body thrust using normal fist)

The procedure for this is basically the same as that for *Seiken-chudan-tsuki;* however, you aim your punch at the facial area.

C. *Seiken-mawashi-uchi* (turning or roundhouse punch with normal fist)

Again, start with the fist in the normal position, but this time twist your body so that your fist is hidden from the opponent. Swing the striking arm outwards from the side in a large half-circle motion and strike the opponent on the side of the head or behind the ear. The twisting of the hips and the snapping back of the other arm is essential for maximum power to be generated in the striking fist. This punch is most useful against a taller attacker.

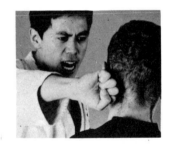

D. *Seiken-ago-uchi* (strike to the jaw with the normal fist)

For this punch, the striking hand is held at shoulder level and close to the body and the wrist is partially turned forward (unlike the previous techniques which have all begun with the hand in the basic position). The power for this punch is created by the sharp pulling back of the other arm simultaneous with the forward thrust. Unlike the previously described punches, this one should be pulled back immediately after striking the object.

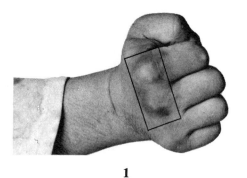

1

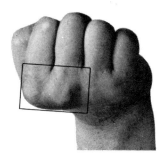

2

2. Uraken (back fist)

There are two basic methods for using this fist. In the first, the fist is clenched in the same way as it is in the *Seiken* position. However, in the *Uraken* position the object is struck by the back of the knuckles rather than the front (1). With this method, the spring action of the wrist facilitates the striking of an opponent who is either very close or at your side.

In the second method (2), the fist is held in the normal position for *Seiken*. The difference is in the thrust, for in this position the punch is delivered with the fist palm up. At the moment of impact, there should be a slight twist in the wrist to maximize this punch's effectiveness.

A. *Uraken-shomen-uchi* (back fist frontal punch)

In this position, the striking fist is held close to the body at about shoulder height, with the back of the hand facing the opponent. The fist is then thrust forward to strike the opponent's face. The actual striking can either be from directly in front or from slightly above, depending upon the degree of bending in the wrist.

B. *Uraken-sayu-uchi* (back fist one-two punch)

Here, the elbows and fists are held at chest height with the back of the hands facing the opponent. Then, using the elbows as pivots, thrust forward and strike with each fist in sequence. These punches are intended mainly for the face, and each should be pulled back immediately after hitting its mark (this will allow for greater speed). Maximum power will be created by the effective twisting of the hips as well as a pushing off from the opponent as each punch is thrown.

C. *Uraken-hizo-uchi* (back fist punch to the spleen)

In the starting position, the fists are held at navel level, one in front of the other. Then, using the elbows as pivots, thrust the fist to the opponent's side (either to the left or right, as needed). The primary target is the gut area.

17

D. *Uraken-shita-tsuki* (back fist lower punch)

This punch is the exact opposite of the *Seiken-chudan-tsuki* in that although the primary positioning and forward thrust are the same, you strike with the fist palm up. It is particularly useful when you are grabbed suddenly by an opponent. Assume a low straddle stance as shown.

3. Tegatana (handsword)

In the handsword (or knifehand) the hand is open. The thumb is bent and held tightly against the edge of the hand. The four fingers are tensed, naturally curved and slightly apart. The outer edge of the hand is primarily used for striking.

A. *Tegatana-sakotsu-uchi* (handsword collar-bone chop)

Hold the striking hand with the palm facing in, on a level with the ear, and swiftly bring the hand forward and down in an arc-like motion in order to hit the opponent's collarbone. Note that the other hand is also held in the *Tegatana* position in preparation for the next blow.

The collarbone is rather weak and a blow to it will cause difficulty in breathing and restriction of arm movement.

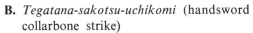

B. *Tegatana-sakotsu-uchikomi* (handsword collarbone strike)

Hold the hand at shoulder height and thrust forward to strike the opponent's collarbone. This differs from the previous technique in that there is more follow-through after the strike.

19

C. *Tegatana-ganmen-uchi* (handsword face chop)

Hold the striking hand as in A (*Tegatana-sakotsu-uchi*). Then bring the hand swiftly down across the face, ear, or neck of an opponent. At the moment of contact, the elbow should be slightly bent.

D. *Tegatana-naka-uchi* (handsword cross-body chop)

Hold the striking hand across your chest at the level of the opposite ear. Then bring the hand diagonally forward across your body in a straight line. The major targets are an opponent's face, neck, throat, and arms.

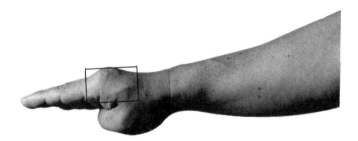

4. Segatana (reverse handsword)

In this position, the thumb is tucked into the palm and it is the inner edge of the hand that is used to strike. *Segatana* may be used from above or from the side; however, strikes thrown in this manner are weaker than those of *Tegatana,* and therefore it is rarely used.

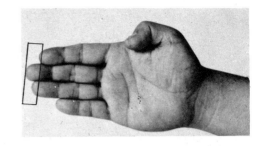

5. Nukite (piercing hand)

In this position, the hand is held in the same manner as in *Tegatana* except that the fingers are not separated. It is important that the fingers never be bent backwards, as serious injuries to the hand can result. The major targets are an opponent's stomach and throat.

A blow to the solar plexus with *Nukite* will render an opponent unconscious. Another common attack point is the lower rib cage (photo A). For the greatest effect, you should aim the blow between two ribs. An expert can nearly penetrate the body with this technique.

An attack to the throat will possibly cause lethal damage as this area is very soft and vulnerable (photo B).

A
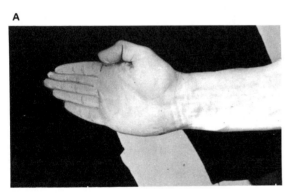

B
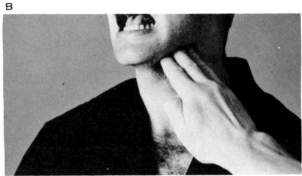

6. Variation of nukite

In this variation, the fingers are bent slightly inwards at the first knuckles. This is used when attacking with a roundhouse blow rather than a straight thrust. It allows for greater power and lessens the danger of a hand injury.

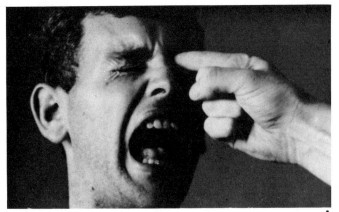

A

7. Ippon-nukite (one-finger piercing hand)

Here, the index finger (forefinger) is extended forward while the other fingers are bent into the palm, and the thumb bends tightly against the side of the middle finger. You thrust with this technique either with the back of the hand facing to the side or facing up. It is used to attack the eye (shown in photo A), below the nose, the throat, or the lower rib area. For best effect, the index finger should be bent very slightly inwards.

B

8. Nihon-nukite (two-finger piercing hand)

Here, the index and middle fingers are extended forward, while the other two fingers are bent with the thumb touching the ring finger.

Photo B illustrates the correct method for striking an opponent's eyes.

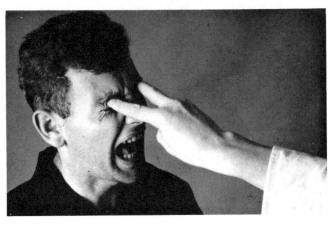

9. Keiko (chicken beak fist)

Bend the four fingers at the knuckles and bring the fingertips together. Then place the thumb underneath the tip of the middle finger. You strike an opponent from above or from the side using a quick snap of the wrist. The major target is the eye (photo A).

10. Oyayubi-ippon-ken (thumb fist)

This is the same as the *Seiken* position except that the thumb tip pushes against the area between

the first and second joints of the index finger, so that the first joint of the thumb sticks out. You strike an opponent with the thumb joint against the temple or below the ear lobe. CAUTION: This punch is extremely dangerous and could easily kill an opponent; therefore, use it with great care, and never make contact during practice.

Photo B illustrates the correct technique for striking the temple from the side.

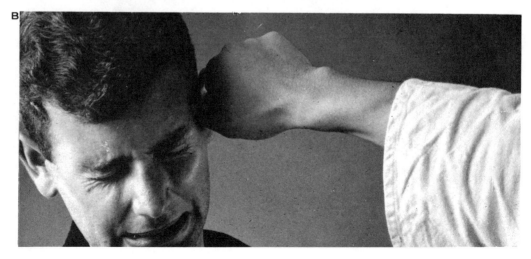

11. Hitosashiyubi-ippon-ken (forefinger fist)

This position is similar to the *Seiken* position, except that the second joint of the index finger should protrude and the thumb should press against the side of the nail of the index finger. You may attack either from above or from directly in front of an opponent. Targets are (A) the lower rib area, (B) beneath the nose, (C) the middle of the forehead, and (D) the throat.

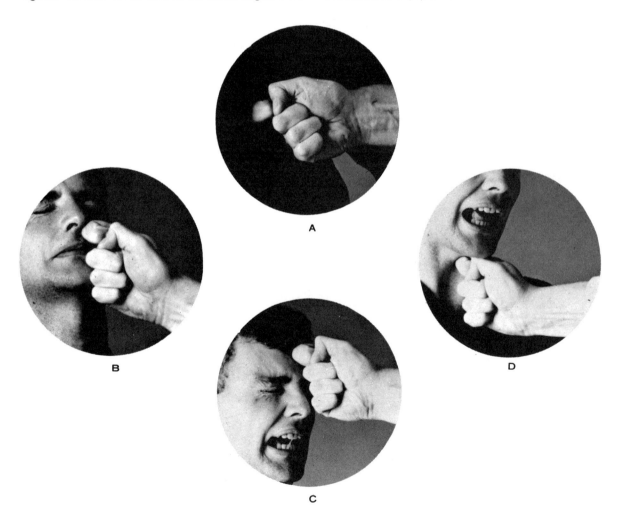

A

B

C

D

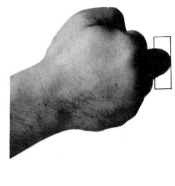

A

12. Nakayubi-ippon-ken (middle-finger fist)

This position is similar to *Hitosashiyubi-ippon-ken* except that it is the second joint of the middle finger which protrudes. The thumb pushes tightly against the area between the first and the second joint of the index finger. Attack procedure and targets are the same as for *Hitosashiyubi-ippon-ken*.

In addition to this position, there is also a combination of *Hitosashiyubi-ippon-ken* and *Nakayubi-ippon-ken* called *Nihon-ken* (two-finger fist), where the second joints of both the index and the middle finger protrude. Also, there is a technique known as *Ryutou-ken* (dragon's head fist), where the middle finger's second joint protrudes to form

the point of a triangle with the other fingers' second knuckles slightly protruding to form the triangle's sides.

Photo A illustrates striking beneath the lower lip using the middle-finger-fist technique.

13. Tettsui (iron hammer fist)

For this technique, the hand is put into the *Seiken* position. However, here it is the meaty outer edge of the hand that is used to strike the opponent. While this is not a sharp blow, it is a heavy and quite powerful weapon. You may attack from above to strike the head or shoulder of an opponent, or from the side in order to strike the temple, neck, or beneath the ear lobe.

B

Photo B illustrates this technique being applied from above to the back of an opponent's neck.

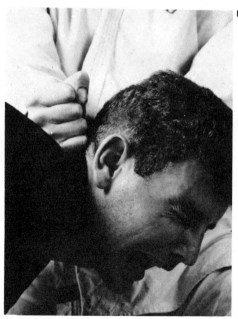

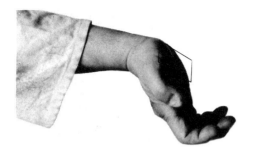

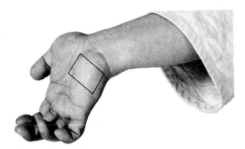

14. Shotei (palm heel thrust)

Here, you use the heel of the hand to strike an opponent. The blow is thrust forward powerfully in a pushing motion. Targets are the face and the jaw. This technique is also used against other areas in defense.

A. *Shotei* to the jaw from below.

B. *Shotei* to the spleen from the side.

C and **D.** The correct stance in preparation for performing the *Shotei-chudan* (middle body palm heel thrust).

E. *Shotei* to the stomach.

A

B

C

D

E

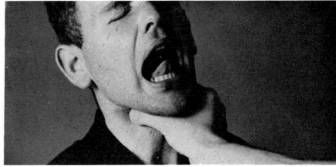

A

15. Toho (sword peak hand)

This is the wedge formed when the thumb is extended away from the rest of the hand. The target for this technique is the throat. Thrust forward and strike the opponent's throat strongly, as shown in photo A.

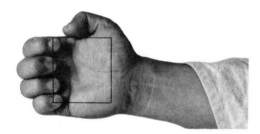

16. Heiken (flat fist)

In this position, the fingers are bent at the second joints as if to make a fist but the tips do not touch the palm. It is the first joints of the fingers and the palm that strike the object. Typical targets are the ear, the cheek, the throat, and the face. CAUTION: When applied to the ear, *Heiken* can rupture the eardrum.

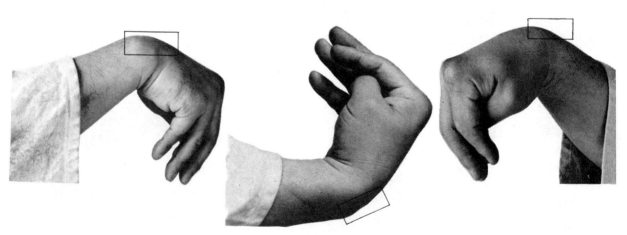

17. Koken (arc fist)

This position is formed by bending the wrist forward, and placing the thumb at the base of the middle finger. An opponent is struck with the exposed outer portion of the wrist. Targets include the spleen, face, and jaw. You can attack from above, below, or from either side of, an opponent. An advanced student can also use this as a defensive technique. Note that this wrist area is very sensitive, and when practicing, you should avoid striking hard objects.

A. *Koken* to the face from above.

B. *Koken* to below the ear lobe from above.

C. *Koken* to the jaw from below.

D. *Koken* to the spleen from the side.

E. *Koken* to the side of the neck with a diagonal blow.

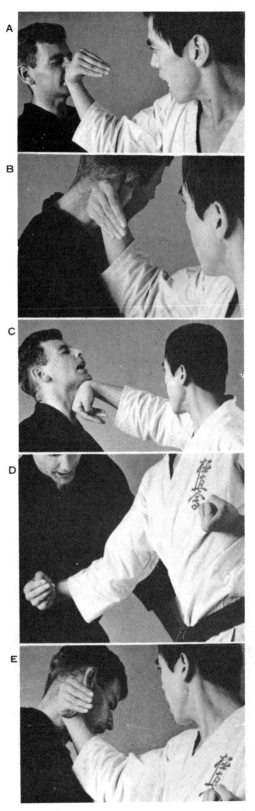

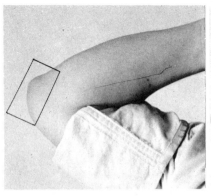
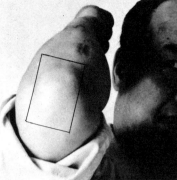
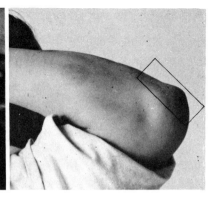

18. Hiji (elbow)

The elbow is considered to be the most devastating weapon in karate. It is a very hard bone and it is close to the shoulder, which generates much of the power for a blow. The elbow is used in four ways: it can strike down on an opponent, or it can strike up, or to the side, or to the back. It is used primarily when an opponent is in close proximity.

A. *Hiji* strike downwards on the back of an opponent's neck.

B. *Hiji* to the opponent's jaw from the side.

C. *Hiji* to the opponent's stomach from the side.

D. *Hiji* to the jaw from below.

A   B   C   D

19. Kote (forearm)

This is the part of the arm between the elbow and the wrist. It is most often used in defense as a block. The fist is held in either the *Seiken* or *Tegatana* positions. As shown in the photos, there are (1) forearm, (2) back forearm, and (3) front forearm. While *Kote* is mostly used for defense, the back forearm position may be used for striking an opponent's jaw.

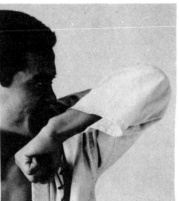

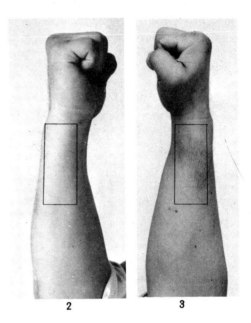

2   3

1

20. Additional upper body weapons

These are the head, the shoulder, and the teeth. The head may strike an object from any direction, but the primary target is an opponent's face. When practicing, do not use the head to strike hard objects. When using the shoulder, be sure to strike with the bony portion.

THE LEG AS A WEAPON

B1

C1

→

D1

→

Due to the fact that the leg is normally used to support the body, it is more awkward to use as a weapon as compared to the arm. However, it is much stronger than the arm, and because of its superior length can be used to attack from a greater distance. It is generally accepted that the leg can express three times as much power as the arm.

A beginner must expect to lose his balance when first learning leg techniques. The three keys to successful mastery are: maintaining the center of gravity by keeping the hips steady, performing the kicks at great speed, and returning the striking leg to the ground immediately after the attack.

When you have developed sufficient strength and flexibility with your legs, you have acquired the strongest weapons in an unarmed man's arsenal. In competition karate, 70 per cent of the winning blows are delivered by the leg.

1. Ashigatana (footsword)

This is the outer edge of the foot, as shown in the photo. It is used to attack the neck, jaw, spleen, hips, and joints.

A

A. *Yoko-geri* (side kick)

Note that in this correct form, each foot and one shoulder form the vertices of a triangle.

B and **C.** *Yoko-geri* (side kicks, front and side views)

First, you transfer your weight to the supporting leg, keeping the hips steady and the knees slightly bent. Then pull up the kicking foot to a position just in front of the knee of the supporting leg. Now, quickly strike out with your leg to the side and immediately return to the starting position.

D. *Kansetsu-geri* (kicks to the knee)

Remember that immediately after delivering a kick, you must return the leg to its starting position. This allows for a quick follow-up kick, and prevents an opponent from catching you off balance.

E. *Ashigatana-yoko-geri-jodan* (upper body side kick using the footsword technique)

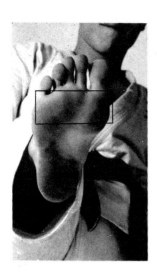

2. Naka-ashi (ball of the foot)

As shown in the photo at the left, this is the fleshy portion, or ball, of the foot just below the toes. In order to strike an opponent without injuring yourself, you must be sure to keep the toes bent back towards the shin. The targets are the temple, face, jaw, chest, and spleen.

A. *Mae-geri-age* (front upper kick)

B. *Chudan-mae-geri* (middle body front kick)

The first step is to bring the knee of the striking leg up above the navel. Then kick forward, striking the opponent's stomach or solar plexus. Be sure to keep the toes bent back to avoid injury. Note that to compensate for the forward kick, you must lean backwards approximately 25° in order to maintain balance. Also, your chest should be slightly concave and your chin tucked into your neck.

C. *Jodan-mae-geri* (upper body front kick)

This technique is basically the same as the previous ones; however, the primary targets are the jaw and face.

A

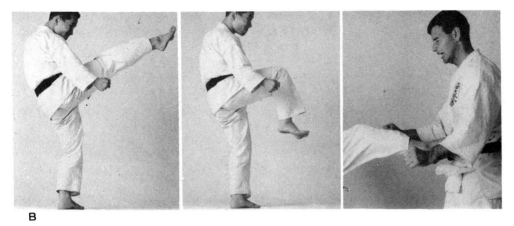

B

D. *Mawashi-geri* (roundhouse kick)

This kick starts in the same position as the above; however, the bent knee is brought to the side and the body is bent away from that

C

side. Then, using a large circular motion, extend your foot forward and strike the jaw, face or side. If the timing is correct, this kick can express a tremendous amount of power.

D

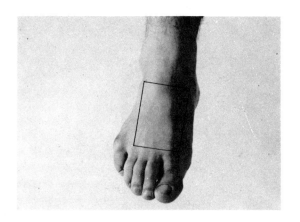
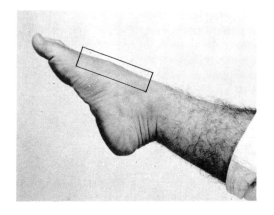

3. Seashi (instep)

As shown in the photos, this is the top of the foot just below the ankle. It is used to strike the groin, side, neck, and ribs. The toes are stretched straight forward.

A. *Mawashi-seashi-geri* (roundhouse kick with the instep)

This technique is basically the same as the turning kick described above, except that an opponent is struck with the instep rather than the ball. The chief target is the neck.

A

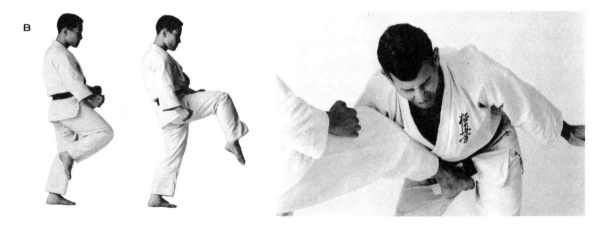

B. *Kinteki-seashi-geri* (testicles kick with the instep)
Bring the knee up and strike forward hitting the opponent's testicles with the instep. CAUTION: This target is the most vulnerable part of the male anatomy, so during practice you should never actually strike a sparring partner. *Kinteki-seashi-geri* is an excellent kick for a woman to use against a real attacker.

4. Soko-ashi (arch)

The arch is usually used for blocking an opponent's attack. It is always better to block a punch with a shock-absorber-like soft area such as the arch, rather than a hard area. This technique is also used to attack an opponent's side or arm with a sweeping sideways motion. (Photos below show front and side views of the *Soko-ashi* defense.)

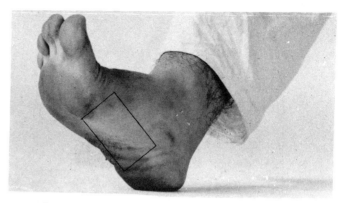

5. Kakato (heel)

The heel is the pivotal point for turning the body. It is also an effective weapon. There are two ways in which it can be used offensively:

A. *Kakato-geri* (heel kick)

This technique is used when the opponent is already on the ground. You bring the leg up, keeping it straight with the toes stretched back. Then bring the heel forcefully down against the opponent's head, face, or stomach. This is a very powerful and dangerous kick as all the body weight is concentrated in the heel.

B. *Ushiro-geri* (rear kick)

This form of attack is used for striking an opponent who is behind you. As illustrated, the correct technique is to drive your momentum backwards and your heel into the stomach of an opponent.

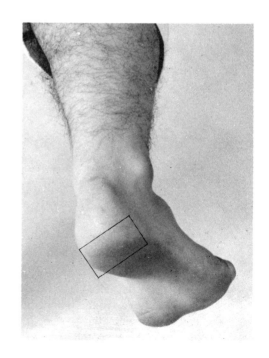

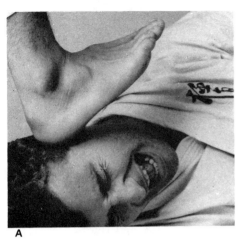

A

B

A. Front and side views of the knee kick using either leg.

6. Hiza-geri (knee kick)

The knee is as hard and powerful as the elbow, and also is most effective when fighting in close. The targets are the testicles, stomach, and thighs.

Another offensive technique is to grasp an opponent's hair and slam his face down against your knee. The knee and upper thigh can also be used defensively to block kicks from an opponent.

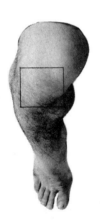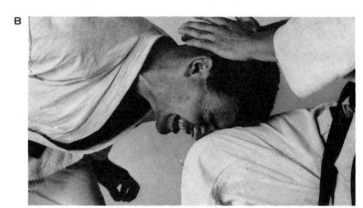

B. Technique of forcing an opponent's face onto your knee.

C. The correct procedure for using the knee kick to attack an opponent's thigh.

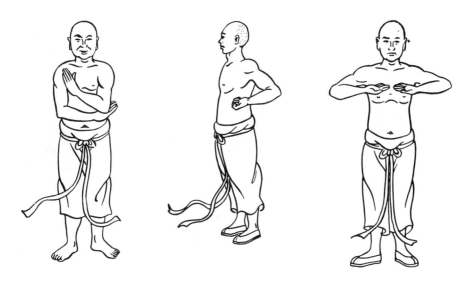

PRELIMINARY EXERCISES

To practice karate effectively and safely, you must first condition your body. These basic exercises should be performed often and repeatedly in order to build up strength and flexibility (and reduce the chances of injuries).

1. Wrist exercises

Start by standing with your legs slightly apart. Then bring your hands together, palms and fingers flat against one another (as shown in photos 1 through 6). Apply pressure and gradually bring your hands to chest level. Then start turning the fingers so that they point upwards, and at the same time raise your hands over your head. Make sure that the two hands always stay in contact with each other. Finally, return the hands to chest level as shown in photo 6.

4

5

6

2. Exercise for the Achilles tendon

Start by standing on your toes. In this position, bend your knees and drop your hips. Then, transfer the body weight to your heels, at the same time straightening your knees but still keeping the hips bent. This is one of the most important of all the preliminary exercises because any sudden strong tension on the Achilles tendon could rupture it. Therefore, it must be strengthened before you attempt any strenuous activities.

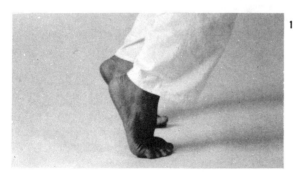

1

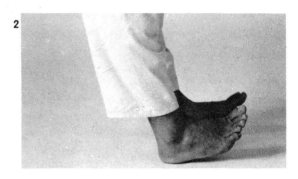

2

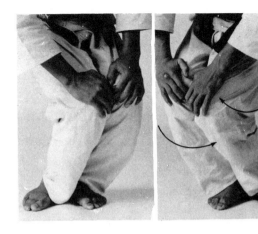

3. Knee exercise

This is primarily a flexibility exercise. Bend the knees deeply, hold them together with both hands, and rotate them to the left and then to the right. Strong, flexible knees are essential as they are the pivotal points for jumping and kicking.

4. Heel and ankle exercise

Lift one foot at a time and rotate the heel in a circular motion to the left and right. This will improve turning and elasticity.

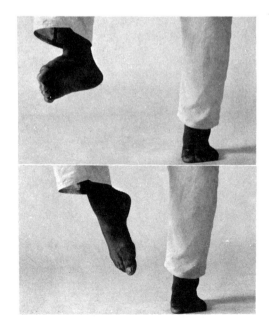

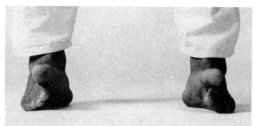 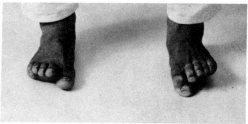

1   2

5. Toe exercise

Stand with the feet slightly spread and the hands grasping the belt. Lift the big toes as far off the ground as possible without lifting the other toes or the rest of the foot.

Then lift the other toes without lifting the big toes. This exercise will reduce the possibility of injuries to the toes resulting from improper kicking techniques, especially when performing *Naka-ashi* (ball-of-the-foot kick).

6. Hip exercise

Stand with the feet wide apart and hands clasped behind your head. Then bend forward without bending your knees, straighten up again, and bend backwards as far as possible. Practice this exercise until you are gradually able to do it with your legs close together.

7. Side exercise for roundhouse block

The roundhouse block (*Mawashi-uke*) is described on page 89. This exercise increases the flexibility and strength of the side muscles. From the starting position (1), pull the lower hand back against the side. Start bending to the side over that hand, and reach up and over the head with the other hand (2). Finally, thrust both hands towards the same side as if to ward off an attacker (3). Return to the starting position and repeat on the opposite side.

8. Back exercise for roundhouse block

Twist your body towards the back as far as possible (1). Then bend forward without bending the knees and touch the ground (2). Return to the standing position. Twist your body in the opposite direction, and repeat the exercise.

9. Push-ups

One variation of the push-up is to use only the fists to push off the ground. In another, your hands are flat against the ground. However, the best method is to use only the fingertips, starting with all five and gradually reducing the number as your strength increases. You should eventually be able to do push-ups with only one finger on each hand. Make sure that your hips neither protrude nor sag when doing this exercise.

10. Leg-stretching exercise

Sit with your legs spread apart as far as possible to either side. Grasp one knee with both hands and gradually pull until your chest is over that knee, being sure you keep the leg flat on the floor. Return to the starting position, place one hand on each ankle, and try to touch your chest to the floor. This exercise is good for stretching the calf and thigh muscles, which will improve the performance of any kicking technique.

11. Neck exercises

These exercises are important for developing a strong, flexible neck, which will protect the part of the spinal cord in this area. The exercises consist of rotating the neck around to the left and right, forward and backwards.

12. Back-stretching exercise

Start with your legs spread wide apart; then bend forward and support yourself on your fists and feet. Now, stretch your upper body as far forward as possible, and arch your back without touching your chest to the floor.

13. Knee-bend exercise

Bend your knees and lower your hips. Place your hands on the tops of the knees and straighten your legs while pushing against the knees. This exercise will aid extension of the legs when performing any of the kicking techniques.

14. Flexibility exercise for the legs

Start by spreading your legs wide apart. Bend one knee, keeping the other knee extended, and lower your body. Place one hand on each knee. Try to touch the calf of the extended leg to the floor by pressing down on the knee with your hand. Avoid leaning too far forward. Repeat the procedure with the other leg.

15. Finger exercise

Start with the fingertips together and gradually bring your hands together until the bases of the fingers (*not* the palms) are touching, by strongly pressing the fingers against each other (your knuckles should "crack").

16. Chest-to-feet exercise

Start in a seated position with the soles of the feet touching. Grasp your feet with both hands and bend the upper body forward until your chest is touching your feet.

17. Shotei-zuke (hip exercise)

This exercise begins in the *Musubi-tachi* stance (described on page 51). Bend your body forward at the waist, and touch the floor with your palms without bending your knees. Place the hands close to the feet and gradually move them until they are behind the feet, still flat on the floor with the fingers pointing back. Vary this exercise by spreading the legs wide apart and placing the right palm in front of the left leg. Repeat with the left hand and the right leg.

49

STANCES

Of primary importance to the successful performing of karate is learning the correct stances. The new student of karate must place himself in the position of a baby and learn to stand all over again. Like the baby's, your mind must be totally receptive to new experiences.

1. Heisoku-tachi (blocked foot stance)

In this stance, the feet are held tightly together with the spine and neck in a straight line. The arms should drop naturally to the sides and the fists should be clenched. In this, as in all stances, you must always face straight ahead and relax the inner self by blocking out all thoughts.

2. Musubi-tachi (open foot stance)

This stance is identical to *Heisoku-tachi* except that the heels are touching, and the toes are separated at a 60° angle. This stance is often used at the beginning of *Kumite* and *Kata*.

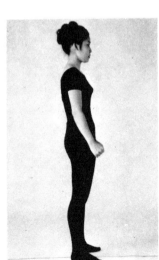

3. Heiko-tachi (parallel foot stance)

The feet are separated to shoulder width and the toes are pointed straight ahead. This is a common stance used for both attacking and defending.

4. Zenkutsu-tachi (forward stance)

In this position, one leg extends behind the body with the knee kept straight and the foot turned outwards. Lean the upper body forward slightly, and bend the front leg. The distance from left to right between the two legs should equal the width of the shoulders.

5. Kokutsu-tachi (back stance)

Extend one leg forward so that only the toes are touching the floor. The back leg is bent and the hips dropped. Two-thirds of the body weight is supported by the back leg. The front foot is pointed to the front and the back foot turned outwards. The legs are shoulder width apart. This stance is used in *Naka-uke* (page 65) and *Tsuki* (page 14).

6. Fudo-tachi (ready stance)

This stance is the same as *Heiko-tachi* except that the feet are both turned outwards. The shoulders should be naturally relaxed as this is a preparative stance for action to follow.

7. Shiko-tachi (Sumo stance)

This is a basic stance derived from Sumo wrestling. The legs are spread apart to twice the width of the shoulders, with the knees bent and the feet turned outwards. The hips are dropped and the spine is straight. The upper body should be supported by the hips. In this position (as well as the next one), the center of gravity is much lower than in most other stances. Therefore, you must have strong legs and hips for good balance. For obvious reasons, this is not a good stance for executing swift kicking techniques.

8. Kiba-tachi (horse stance)

This stance is the same as *Shiko-tachi* except that the feet are pointed forward and tension is placed on the inner parts of the feet. The position is similar to that of riding a horse.

9. Sansen-tachi (fighting stance)

This is a common practice stance. One foot is placed one step forward so that its heel is on the same horizontal line as the toes of the back foot. Both feet are turned in. The distance between the toes of each foot is shoulder width. The tension is placed along the inner edges of the feet, allowing for a very stable posture.

The photos below show how to convert from *Heiko-tachi* (see page 52) to *Sansen-tachi* by bringing one foot towards the other using a circular motion so that the feet briefly touch and then separate. The moving foot should end up one step in front and to the side of the stationary foot.

10. Tsuru-ashi-tachi (crane stance)

Here, the body is supported on one leg. The sole of the raised foot is placed against the inside of the knee, like a crane standing on one leg. In this stance, you should be ready to strike with *Yoko-geri* (side kick) and *Uraken* (back fist). This is a transitional stance between a period of defense and attack.

11. Naka-hachiji-tachi (inner figure 8 stance)

This is named for the resemblance of the position of the feet to the Japanese character for the numeral 8. The feet are shoulder width apart, with the toes turned in and the heels turned out. The tension should be placed along the inner edges of the feet, spine, and the sides.

12. Soto-hachiji-tachi (outer figure 8 stance)

This is similar to *Fudo-tachi* (ready stance) except that the feet are wider apart and therefore the stance is more stable.

13. Kake-ashi-tachi (hooked foot stance)

Like *Tsuru-ashi-tachi,* this is a transitional stance used to smooth out conversions from one movement to another. Starting from any stance, move one leg backwards and place it as if hooking it behind the knee of the other leg. Only the toes touch the ground—the back of the foot should be raised. This stance enables you to do one of two things—to either drop back one step or to prepare for executing a kick.

14. Futa-ashi-tachi (two-legged stance)

Stand with the feet one shoulder width apart. Place one foot just in front of the other with the toes pointing forward. The knees should be relaxed, making this a rather loose and versatile preparative stance.

15. Neko-ashi-tachi (cat stance)

This stance is very similar to *Kokutsu-tachi* except that the distance between the front and back feet is narrower. Ninety per cent of the body weight is supported by the back leg. Because the front leg is held very loosely, its great flexibility allows for very successful kicks. It is generally true that the narrower the stance, the faster the leg action.

 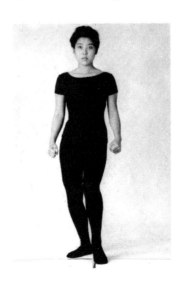 

16. Shumoku-tachi or Toboku-tachi (T-shaped stance)

Place one foot with the toes pointing straight forward. Place the second foot perpendicular to the first, making a 90° angle. The heels of both feet are touching, and the body faces directly forward.

UKE (DEFENSE)

You should never feel that defense means passivity and accept the rôle of the underdog; instead, confidently expect to win every fight. You can never improve without absolute belief in your own abilities.

A

B

C

D

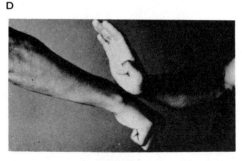

E

1. Defense against hand attacks

You must develop your defense techniques so that they become the first step in a counter-attack. Every block should be transformed into some sort of offensive weapon. With this in mind, you can understand the importance of thoroughly mastering the basic defense techniques.

A. *Chudan-tsuki* (middle body thrust) blocked by *Shotei* (palm heel thrust) to the inside.

B. The same defense except that the thrust is blocked to the outside.

C. A thrust blocked by *Tegatana* (handsword).

D. A punch blocked by *Shotei* (palm heel thrust) from above.

E. A punch blocked by *Tegatana-kake* (handsword hook). This block is the same as C except that the wrist is turned inwards. with the palm facing down.

F. A punch blocked to the outside with *Koken* (arc fist).

G. *Koken* from above.

H. *Koken* from below.

I. *Hirate-tsukami* (flat hand grasp)
Even though this is called a "grasp," it is actually

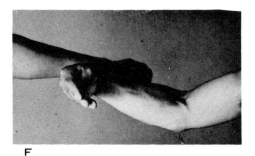

F

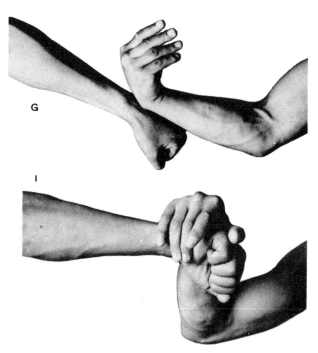

G

H

I

only a hooking block. As you can see in the photo, the thumb and the fingers do not close around the

opponent's fist but merely swat it away. This technique is used very often.

2. Defense against leg attacks

For defending against kicking attacks, you can use either your arms or legs. However, the arms are used to block more often because leg blocks are much slower, although timing can be greatly improved by constant practice.

A. *Mawashi-geri* (roundhouse kick) blocked by *Hidari-jodan-heiko-uke* (upper body parallel block using the left hand) to the right leg.

B. *Mawashi-geri* (roundhouse kick) blocked by *Jodan-heiko-soto-uke* (upper body parallel block to the inside) to the left leg using the left hand.

A

B

C. *Mae-geri* (front kick) blocked by *Gedan-barai* (lower body sweep).

D. *Mae-geri* (front kick) blocked by *Shotei-uke* (palm heel block).

E. *Mae-geri* (front kick) blocked by *Gedan-juji-uke* (lower body X-block).

F. *Mae-geri* (front kick) blocked by *Gedan-tegatana-juji-uke* (lower body handsword X-block).

G. *Mae-geri* (front kick) blocked by *Soko-ashi-naka-uke* (arch block to the outside).

H. *Mae-geri* (front kick) blocked by *Hiza-soto-uke* (knee block from the outside).

C

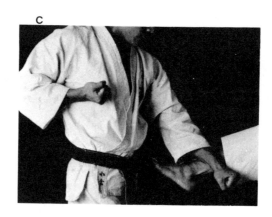

D

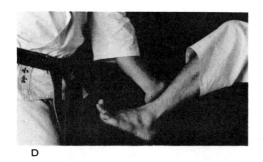

E

F

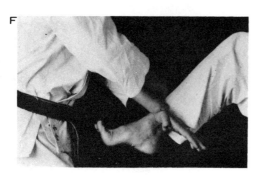

G

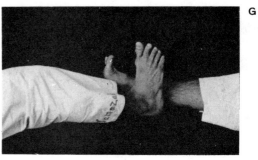

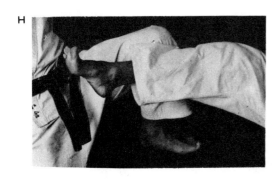

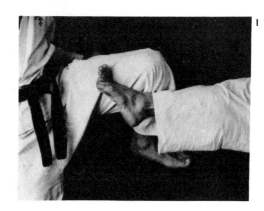

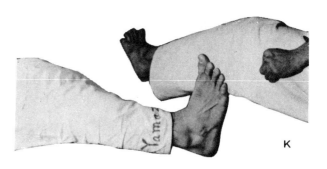

I. *Mae-geri* (front kick) blocked by *Hiza-naka-uke* (knee block to the outside).

J. *Mae-geri* (front kick) blocked by the shin from the inside.

K. *Mae-geri* (front kick) blocked by an arch block to the inside.

L. *Mae-geri* (front kick) blocked by the shin to the inside.

3. Applying blocking techniques

A. *Jodan-uke* (upper body block)

In the correct position for this technique (shown here), the blocking hand is held at a distance of two fists from the head, while the other hand is held at chest level.

(1) *Jodan-tsuki* (upper body thrust) blocked by *Jodan-uke* (upper body block).

(2) Various applications of *Jodan-uke*.

①

②

B. *Soto-uke* (block from the outside)
(1) In the performance of this block, the blocking hand is rotated from a position next to the ear to a point in front of the eyes. The other hand remains at chest level.
(2) In this block, you should use the muscular area below the elbow when making actual contact. For the most effective block of a punch, always aim for the opponent's wrist (this is very important to remember).

C. *Naka-uke* (block from the inside)
(1) *Chudan-tsuki* (middle body thrust) blocked from the inside.
(2) When you anticipate a very powerful punch, support the blocking arm with your other arm.

①

②

①

②

③

D. *Tegatana-jodan-uke* (handsword upper body block)

(1) Side view of *Tegatana-jodan-uke* using the left arm.

(2) *Tegatana-jodan-uke* from the front.

(3) *Jodan-tsuki* (upper body thrust) blocked by *Tegatana-jodan-uke* to the outside.

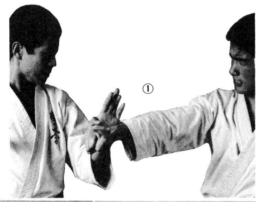

①

②

E. *Shotei-uke* (palm heel block)

(1) *Shotei-sotogawa-uke* (palm heel block from the outside).

(2) *Shotei-shita-uke* (palm heel block from above).

(3) Side and front view of *Shotei-uke*.

③

F. *Tegatana-uke* (handsword block).

(1) *Tegatana-uke* with the left hand.
(2) *Migi-jodan-tsuki* (upper body thrust with the right hand) blocked by *Hidari-tegatana-soto-uke* (handsword block from the outside with the left hand).

(3) *Chudan-tsuki* (middle body thrust) blocked by *Tegatana-gedan-barai* (lower body sweep).
(4) Transition from *Tegatana-jodan-uke* (upper body handsword block) to *Kake-uke* (hook block).

G. *Koken-ue-uke* (arc fist block from below)

This technique is used more to deflect, rather than block, an opponent's punch.

(1) A right-hand punch blocked by *Koken* (arc fist) with the left hand.
(2) *Koken-ue-uke* as seen from the front and the side.

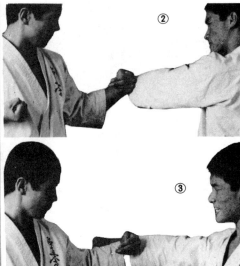

① ②

③ ①

H. *Koken-yoko-uke* (arc fist block to the side)
(1) Front and side views.
(2) A left middle body elbow attack blocked by *Koken-chudan-naka-uke* (arc fist middle body block to the outside).

(3) A right-hand middle body punch blocked by *Koken-chudan-naka-uke* (arc fist middle body block from the inside).

I. *Koken-oroshi-uke* (arc fist block from above)
(1) This technique resembles *Koken-oroshi-uchi* (arc fist attack from above).

(2) *Migi-chudan-tsuki* (middle body punch with the right hand) blocked by *Koken-oroshi-uke* with the left hand.

① ②

①

②

J. *Segatana-uke* (reverse handsword block)
(1) *Chudan-tsuki* (middle body thrust) blocked by *Segatana-uke* from the outside.
(2) *Chudan-tsuki* blocked by *Hidari-segatana-uke* (reverse handsword block with the left hand). When an opponent's punch is very strong, you can strengthen your block by supporting the blocking arm with your other hand. This is a very powerful defense.

K. *Shotei-ue-uke* (palm heel block from below)
(1) Front view.
(2) *Migi-jodan-tsuki* (upper body thrust with the right hand) blocked by *Shotei-ue-uke* with the left hand.

①

②

L. *Gedan-barai* (lower body sweep)
(1) Front view.
(2) Side view.
(3) A middle body punch blocked by *Gedan-barai*.

(4) During practice, start in *Sansen-tachi* (fighting stance). An opponent's left-hand punch should be blocked by the right hand from the inside, and a right-hand punch should be blocked by the left hand, also from the inside.
(5) *Gedan-barai* (with the left hand) and *Migi-naka-uke* (right block from the inside) being performed (front and side views).

M. *Jodan-juji-uke* (upper body X-block)
(1) *Jodan-tsuki* (upper body thrust) blocked by *Juji-uke* (X-block).

(2) *Jodan-tsuki* blocked by *Tegatana-juji-uke* (X-block using the handsword technique).

2. Application of Fundamental Techniques

第三章　基本の応用

Karate is made up of four basic movements: forward, backwards, turning and jumping. However, you should avoid moving backwards whenever possible, and strive to keep the direction of attack forward, blocking as you go. Rather than retreating backwards under the assault of an opponent, turn to the side in order to throw him off balance, or block the attack and convert your block into an offensive weapon. You should enter every combat with the idea that there is no retreat; the momentum of battle should always be forward.

OI-TSUKI (LUNGE PUNCH)

This is a type of "shadow boxing" using karate techniques. You perform a series of from 3 to 5 attacks and blocks while moving forward, and conclude with a turn. Although you practice these moves alone, you must feel as though you were actually fighting a live opponent, and try to project a sense of tremendous power.

Turning

Even though it has been taught in all karate schools that basic techniques for attacking and blocking an opponent follow a straight-line progression, actually the more natural and effective technique is a circular movement. This should, therefore, be stressed during every practice session.

1. Chudan-oi-tsuki (middle body lunge punch)

Begin in *Fudo-tachi* (ready stance) (1), then move the right leg one step back and pull the right fist against the right side of the chest. The left arm is in *Hidari-gedan-barai* (left lower body sweep) position (2). From here, move the right leg one step forward and perform *Migi-chudan-seiken-tsuki* (right middle body thrust with normal fist) (3). Then repeat this procedure with the left leg and arm as you move another step forward (left middle body thrust with normal fist) (4).

2. Turn after Chudan-oi-tsuki (middle body lunge punch)

No matter how many times you perform *Chudan-oi-tsuki,* eventually you must turn around. At the moment that you have made the last blow with the right hand, move the rear (left) leg across to the right and pivot 180° on both feet at the same time, while performing *Hidari-gedan-barai* (left lower body sweep). This will exactly reverse your position. From here, continue *Chudan-oi-tsuki* and repeat the entire series back and forth several times.

3. Chudan-gyaku-oi-tsuki (middle body lunge punch from the reverse position)

This is the same as *Chudan-oi-tsuki* except that the right arm thrust coincides with the left leg forward step, and vice versa.

4. Jodan-oi-gyaku-tsuki (upper body lunge punch from the reverse position)

This technique is the same as *Chudan-gyaku-oi-tsuki,* except that the arm thrusts are directed towards the head of an opponent. The turning technique is the same as the one previously described.

74

5. Chudan-soto-uke (middle body block from the outside)

This is the same as *Chudan-oi-tsuki* except that instead of an offensive attack, you are performing a defensive block from the outside. When turning at the end of one forward sequence, you pull the left leg to the back and go into the left forward stance (*Hidari-zenkutsu-tachi*).

6. Chudan-gyaku-soto-uke (middle body block from the outside from the reverse position)

This defense is the same as *Chudan-soto-uke* except that the right arm block coincides with the forward step of the left leg, and vice versa.

7. Jodan-uke (upper body block)

This is a defensive technique for blocking blows from above. The basic procedure is the same as for those previously mentioned, except that the block is aimed higher.

8. Jodan-gyaku-uke (upper body block from the reverse position)

This is the same as *Jodan-uke* except that the right hand block is coincidental with the forward step of the left leg.

9. Zenkutsu-hiji-age-uchi (forward elbow upper thrust)

Starting from a forward stance, perform a lower body sweep, then put the right leg forward, and at the same time perform an elbow upper thrust with the right arm. Then continue on, moving to the other side.

10. Zenkutsu-gyaku-hiji-age-uchi (forward elbow upper thrust from the reverse position)

This is the same as *Zenkutsu-hiji-age-uchi* except that the right elbow thrust coincides with the forward step of the left leg, and vice versa.

11. Hiji-soto-uchi (elbow thrust from the outside)

This technique is very similar to *Zenkutsu-hiji-age-uchi* except that the thrust is performed to the front and side of an opponent's head in a sweeping motion. The leg and arm movements are the same as in 9.

12. Hiji-gyaku-soto-uchi (elbow thrust from the outside from the reverse position)

This is the same as *Hiji-soto-uchi* except that the right elbow outer thrust coincides with the forward step of the left leg, and vice versa.

13. Sansen-tsuki (fighting blow)

Starting from the *Sansen-tachi* (fighting stance), perform *Migi-chudan-tsuki* (right middle body thrust). Repeat with *Hidari-chudan-tsuki* (left middle body thrust).

14. Sansen-gyaku-tsuki (fighting blow from the reverse position)

This technique is the same as the previous one except that the right arm thrust coincides with the forward step of the left leg, and vice versa.

15. Turn after Sansen-tsuki (fighting blow)

Starting from the fighting stance with the right leg slightly in front (right fighting stance), pivot on the left leg 180° to the left and end up in the left fighting stance.

16. Tegatana-uke (handsword block)

From *Hidari-gedan-barai* (left lower body sweep position), step forward with the right leg; this is the back stance (*Kokutsu-tachi*). At the same time, bring the right hand forward in *Tegatana-uke*. Continue, alternating left and right.

18. Shotei-uke (palm heel block)

Stand in either the back stance or the cat stance, and perform a left lower body sweep (*Hidari-gedan-barai*). Then, put the right leg one step forward and perform a right palm heel block. Continue, alternating left to right.

17. Turn after Tegatana-uke (handsword block)

Starting from left *Tegatana-uke* (this is the position you should be in at the end of one complete series), turn to the right by pivoting 180° on both heels. At the same time, gradually reverse the position of the hands so that you end up in right *Tegatana-uke* position.

19. Shotei-gyaku-uke (palm heel block from the reverse position)

This is the same as *Shotei-uke* except that the right *Shotei-uke* coincides with the forward step of the left leg, and vice versa.

20. Segatana-uke (reverse hand-sword block)

This technique is the same as *Shotei-uke* except that a reverse handsword is performed instead of a palm heel block.

21. Koken-uke (arc fist block)

This is the same as *Shotei-uke* except that an arc fist block is performed. The blocking hand should be held at eye level. (Both 20 and 21 may be performed from the reverse position.)

22. Kaiten-jun-tsuki (turn and thrust)

Start by performing a lower-body sweep (*Hidari-gedan-barai*) with the left hand; then begin to step forward with the right leg while pivoting 90° on the left leg. At the end of the pivot, the right leg should be very close to the left leg, but still not touching the ground. From here, thrust forward both the right leg and arm. You should now be in a horse stance, one foot in a direct line with the other. Continue, alternating from left to right. Note that this technique is very fast; even though it looks like a long time is taken to perform a single pivot and thrust, actually this is almost instantaneous.

OI-GERI (LUNGE KICK)

1. Oi-mae-geri (front lunge kick)

Starting with a lower body sweep (*Hidari-gedan-barai*), with the arms held loosely, kick with the right leg to the opponent's chest. It is important when performing this to bring down the kicking leg very gently to avoid injury to the foot. Continue, alternating the kicks from the left leg to the right leg.

2. Oi-mae-geri-age (front lunge upper kick)

This technique is the same as *Oi-mae-geri* except that you aim the kick higher, towards an opponent's face and head.

3. Oi-yoko-geri-age (side lunge upper kick)

Starting from the horse stance (*Kiba-tachi*), pivot 180° on the left leg and perform a side kick with the right leg. Continue, alternating the legs from left to right. Make sure that you drop your kicking leg gently after kicking.

4. Oi-mawashi-geri (roundhouse lunge kick)

Start as in *Oi-mae-geri* (front lunge kick), move the right leg forward using a circular motion and strike an opponent's jaw with *Naka-ashi* (ball of the foot). Continue, alternating legs.

5. Oi-ashigatana (lunge foot-sword)

Starting from *Han-kiba-tachi* (half horse stance), pivot 180° on the left leg and perform a footsword kick to the side with the right leg. Continue, alternating legs.

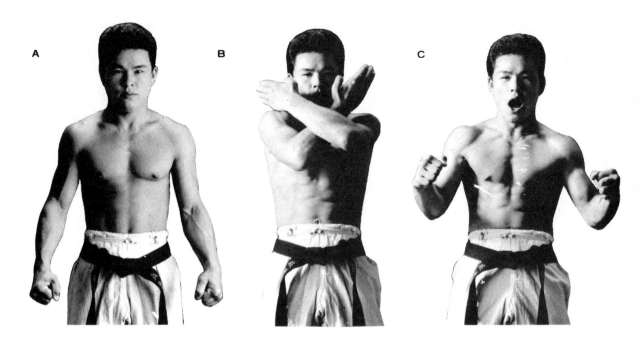

A   B   C

BREATHING

One of the most important aspects of karate is breathing correctly. The average person uses his lungs to only 60 per cent of their full capacity, and it is essential for the karateka (one who practices karate) to improve upon this. The part of the body that is particularly affected by breathing is the lower abdomen, which is 5 to 10 cm below the navel. The muscle found in this area must be very strong and taut in order to perform karate with the utmost effectiveness, and the correct breathing technique will improve the muscle tone of this area greatly. Of course, correct breathing will also improve the whole body, as well as the mind.

1. Ibuki

This series of breathing techniques is called *Ibuki* in karate, and should be practiced repeatedly on a daily basis. (The pictures at the bottom of the pages show side views of *Ibuki*.)

A–B: Stand with both hands clenched tightly, and inhale so quietly that no one will be able to hear you. As you inhale, gradually bring your arms up and cross them on either side of the head. Inhale slowly and fully, all the time trying to force the air down into the lower abdomen.

C–D: When you have inhaled to your fullest capacity, exhale noisily, trying to force the air out by using the lower abdomen. While exhaling, uncross your arms and clench your fists and gradually lower them to your sides. Towards the end of the exhalation, tense all the muscles in the body, especially in the abdomen.

E: The body at the completion of one breathing cycle.

D

E

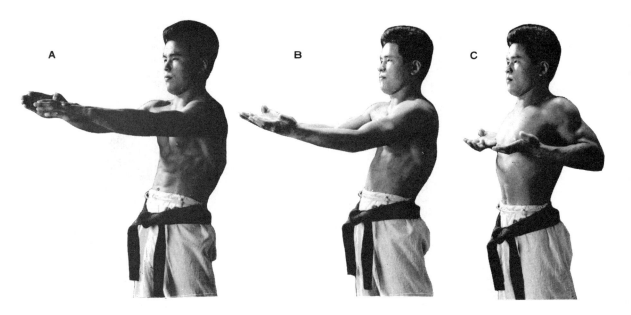

2. Front breathing

A. Stretch both arms out to the front.

B. Turn both hands palm upwards.

C. Inhale deeply in a quiet manner as you gradually bring both hands back to your chest.

D. Lower the hands gradually.

E. Turn the hands palms down and begin to exhale quietly. Continue lowering the hands.

F. Completion of one breathing cycle.

In combat you must exhale silently so that your opponent will not know when you are out of breath—at the end of an exhalation the body is very vulnerable. For one thing, movements and reactions are slowed down, and for another, blows to the body at this time produce the greatest shock to the system. When there is air in the lower abdominal area, blows to the body do not produce so great a shock. For these reasons, you should exercise so that you can prolong the period of time that air remains in the lower abdomen.

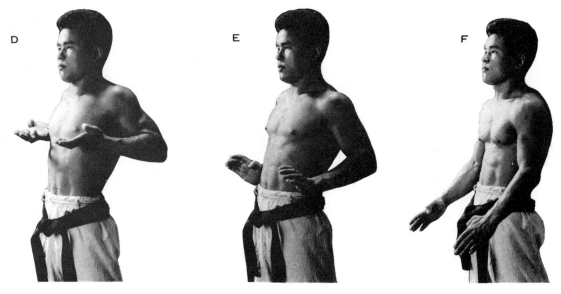

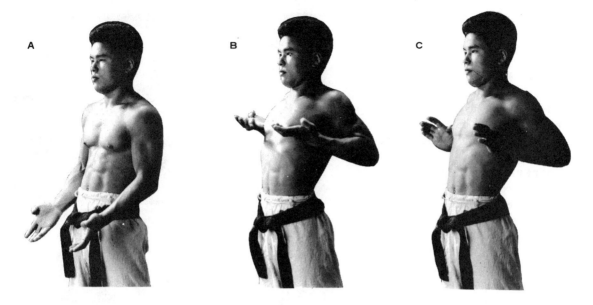

3. Back breathing

The repeated practice of this exercise is very important for the best performance in karate.

A. Stand with the arms bent slightly at the elbow and the hands held with the palms up.

B. Start to inhale, gradually bringing the hands up to shoulder level.

C. At the peak of inhalation, stop, and tense all the muscles, especially the elbows, legs, and middle fingers. Gradually turn the hands palm down.

D. Gradually lower the hands but keep the fingers tensed as if you were going to thrust them at an opponent.

E. Holding your breath, tense the lower abdomen, sides, and fingertips, and extend the hands forward.

F. From this position, relax and exhale, gradually lowering your arms to the position in A (palms should gradually be turned up).

THE POINT AND CIRCLE

As was previously mentioned, although many schools of karate stress linear motion, actually the most effective techniques are those that utilize circular movements. It is interesting to note that the martial arts in India and China stress circular movements.

According to studies in kinetic energy, the greater the centrifugal force present the greater the distance the circumference of a circle is from a center. Therefore, the karateka should think of his hips as the center of a circle and perform his punches as though outlining the circumference of a large circle. This will make for much more powerful blows than punches thrown in a direct linear fashion.

The techniques in the photos here illustrate this concept of performing punches, blocks and sweeps in a circular or curvilinear motion.

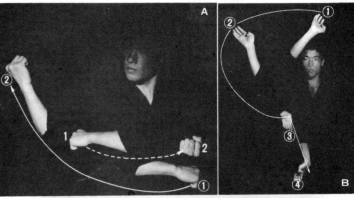

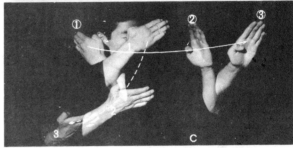

A. *Chudan-naka-uke* (middle body block from the inside)

B. *Enkei-shotei-shita-uke* (palm heel block from above in a circular motion)

C. *Tegatana-naka-uchi* (handsword cross body chop from the inside)

D. *Koken-shotei-uke* (arc fist-palm heel block)

E. *Jodan-uke* (upper body block)

F. *Jodan-seiken-tsuki* (upper body thrust using normal fist)

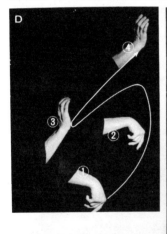

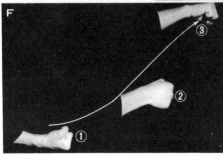

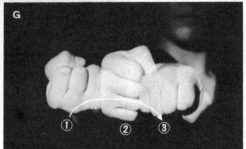

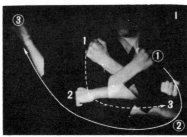

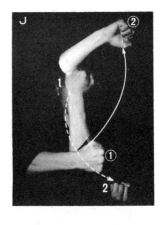

G. *Jodan-seiken-tsuki* (front view)

At the instant that the fist comes in contact with the object, it should be twisted as illustrated.

H. *Gedan-oroshi* (lower body drop punch)

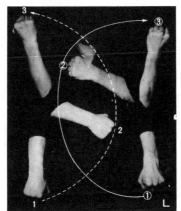

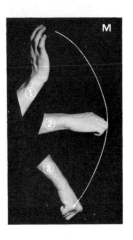

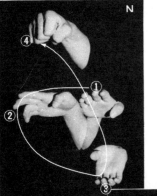

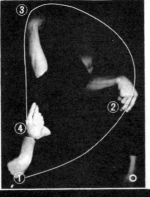

I. *Chudan-naka-uke* (middle body block from the inside)

J. *Jodan-uke* (upper body block)

K. *Gedan-barai* (lower body sweep)

L. *Chudan-naka-uke* (middle body block from the inside) to both sides

M. *Sage-uchi* (drop punch)

N. *Tegatana-urakake-ue-tsuki* (hand-sword back hook-upper punch)

O. *Enkei-koken-shita-uchi* (lower punch using the arc fist in a circular motion)

P. *Omote-urakake* (front-back hook)

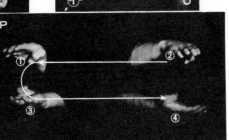

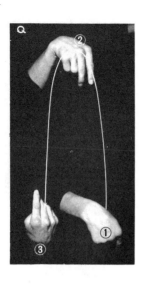

Q. *Kaiten-koken-mawashi-oroshi-uchi* (turning arc fist drop punch)

R. *Sotote-kake-oroshi-uchi* (outer hand hook drop punch)

S. *Tegatana-urakake-ue-tsuki* (hand-sword hook-upper punch)

T. *Age-uchi* (rising strike)

U. *Koken-enkei-ue-tsuki* (arc fist upper punch in a circular motion)

V. *Koken-shotei-uke* (arc fist-palm heel block)

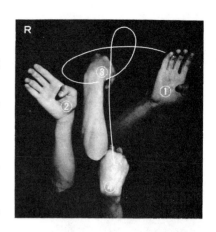

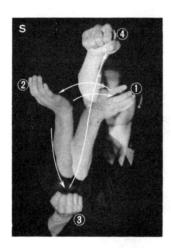

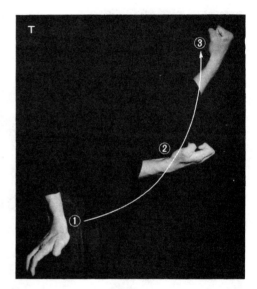

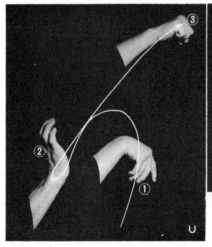

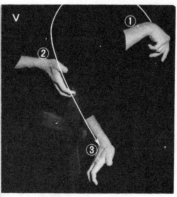

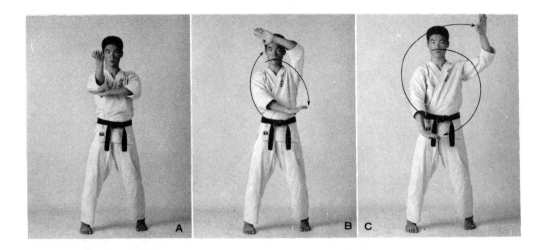

MAWASHI-UKE (ROUNDHOUSE BLOCK)

This block is one of the most important blocks in all of karate.

1. Migi-mawashi-uke (right roundhouse block)

A. Starting from the parallel stance, raise your right arm and bend it at the elbow. The elbow should be on a level with the chest. Next, bring the left hand across the front of the chest, turn it palm down and touch the elbow of the right arm with the wrist of the left hand.

B. The right arm is now extended downwards in a circular motion, while the left arm is being brought up with the hands crossing in front of the face.

C. The right hand is now extended straight downwards, while the left arm has continued in its circular path across the face and out to the side.

D. The hands are now in position to block punches: the right hand at shoulder level protects the upper body and face, the left hand in the hip area protects the lower body and genital area. Both defenses rely on the heels of the hands for maximum protection.

E. After the blocks have been performed, both arms are extended forward with the heels of both hands protruding in *Shotei-oshi* (palm heel thrust).

F. Side view of E.

F'. The progression of the hands into *Shotei-oshi* (palm heel thrust).

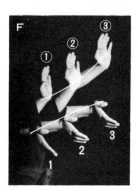

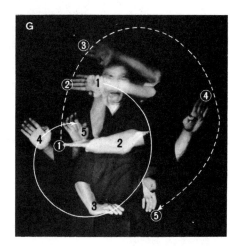

2. Hidari-mawashi-uke (left roundhouse block)

This is the same as the right roundhouse block except that it is performed in the opposite direction, as shown in G'.

ENKEI-GYAKU-TSUKI (REVERSE THRUST IN A CIRCULAR MOTION)

1. Migi-enkei-gyaku-tsuki (right reverse thrust in a circular motion)

This technique is especially useful when you are attacked from behind or from the side. When attacked in this manner, you twist your body and perform the *Tegatana-kake* (handsword hook). This technique forces you to make a 180° turn, and constant practice will sharpen your reaction time for all movements of this kind.

A. Starting in the forward stance, bring your left hand in front of the genital area in order to protect it.

B. Start moving the left arm up in the circular motion.

C. Begin to twist your body towards the left side as the arm moves back.

D. Then, block the opponent's thrust with *Tegatana-kake* (handsword hook).

E. Pulling the opponent off balance with the hook, attack with the right arm.

2. Hidari-enkei-gyaku-tsuki (left reverse thrust in a circular motion)

This is the same technique performed in the opposite direction.

A

TEGATANA-UKE (HANDSWORD BLOCK)

Of all the blocks in karate, the handsword block is the one used most often. This block should be performed in a semi-circular motion in order for it to be most successful. Again, we emphasize the fact that circular movements are essential for maximum effectiveness in karate.

1. Migi-tegatana-uke (right handsword block)

A. In the back stance, bring both hands to a position in front of the genital area.

B. Swing both hands backwards and to the left side of the body.

C. Continue following a circular path until the hands are on a level with the left ear.

D. At this point, the right hand crosses over in front of the face and starts to descend. The left hand begins to drop towards the chest.

E. The right hand is now in position to block the thrust and the left hand is guarding the vital areas of the body.

F. Follow carefully the circular patterns of the hands shown here.

B

C

D

E

F

2. Hidari-tegatana-uke (left hand-sword block)

A. This is the exact opposite of *Migi-tegatana-uke* (right handsword block). Stand in the left back stance, and bring both hands to a position in front of *Kinteki* (groin).

B. Swing both hands backwards and to the right side of the body.

C. Continue following a circular motion until the hands are on a level with the right ear.

D. At this point, the left hand crosses over in front of the face and starts to descend. The right hand begins to drop towards the chest.

E. The left hand is now in position to block the thrust and the right hand is guarding the vital areas of the body.

F. The circular movements of the hands.

RHYTHM IN KARATE

Rhythm is defined as any kind of movement characterized by the regular recurrence of strong and weak elements. All things in the universe have rhythm, either external, like music, or internal, like the atomic structure of a rock. The martial arts are no exception, and the student who has a sense of rhythm will improve in karate much more quickly than one who does not. It would be of great assistance to a karateka to become involved in the rhythmic occurrences in everyday life such as music, dance, and so on. This will lead to a unification of the mind and body which will serve as the firm foundation for growth and excellence in any undertaking.

3. Kata

第四章
型（かた）

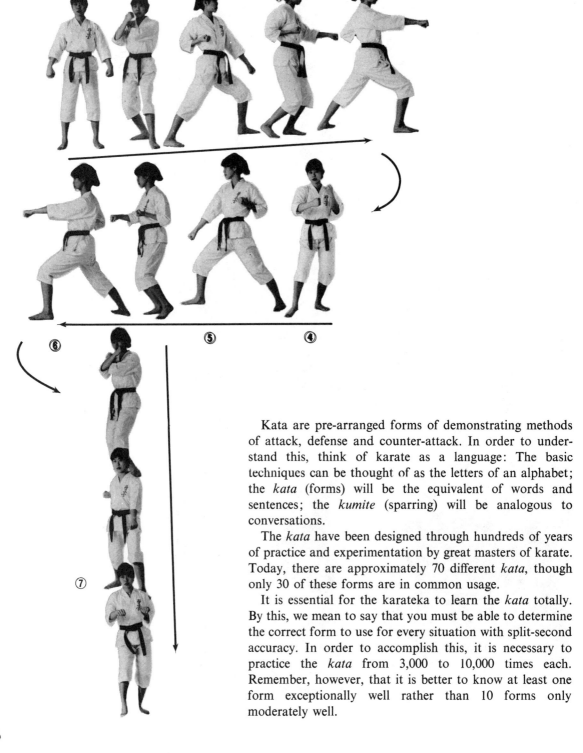

Kata are pre-arranged forms of demonstrating methods of attack, defense and counter-attack. In order to understand this, think of karate as a language: The basic techniques can be thought of as the letters of an alphabet; the *kata* (forms) will be the equivalent of words and sentences; the *kumite* (sparring) will be analogous to conversations.

The *kata* have been designed through hundreds of years of practice and experimentation by great masters of karate. Today, there are approximately 70 different *kata*, though only 30 of these forms are in common usage.

It is essential for the karateka to learn the *kata* totally. By this, we mean to say that you must be able to determine the correct form to use for every situation with split-second accuracy. In order to accomplish this, it is necessary to practice the *kata* from 3,000 to 10,000 times each. Remember, however, that it is better to know at least one form exceptionally well rather than 10 forms only moderately well.

TAIKYOKU 1

1. Start in the *Fudo-tachi* stance (ready stance).

2. Turn to the left and assume the *Hidari-zenkutsu-tachi* (left forward stance) while performing *Hidari-gedan-barai* (left lower body sweep).

3. Take one step forward with the right foot and perform the *Chudan-tsuki* (middle body thrust).

4. Swing the body around to the right 180° in preparation for . . .

5. . . . *Migi-gedan-barai* (right lower body sweep).

6. Perform a *Hidari-oi-tsuki* (left lunge punch).

7. Bring the left foot back next to the right. Turn and step to the left (left foot should be at a 90° angle to the right foot) and perform *Hidari-gedan-barai* (left lower body sweep).

8. Step forward with the right foot and perform *Migi-seiken-chudan-oi-tsuki* (right middle body lunge punch using the normal fist).

9. Step forward with the left foot and perform *Hidari-seiken-chudan-oi-tsuki* (left middle body lunge punch using the normal fist).

10. Step forward with the right foot and perform *Migi-seiken-chudan-oi-tsuki* (right middle body lunge punch using the normal fist).

11. Pivot 270° to the left on the right foot (the left foot should now be in front). Then, perform *Hidari-gedan-barai* (left lower body sweep).

12. Perform *Migi-chudan-oi-tsuki* (right middle body lunge punch).

13. After performing *Migi-chudan-oi-tsuki,* swing the right arm to the right and perform *Migi-gedan-barai* (right lower body sweep). This entails pivoting 180° to the right on the left foot.

14. Take one step forward and perform *Hidari-seiken-chudan-oi-tsuki* (left middle body lunge punch using the normal fist).

15. Bring the left foot back next to the right. Turn and step with the left leg 90° to the left and perform *Hidari-gedan-barai* (left lower body sweep).

16. Step forward and perform *Migi-seiken-chudan-oi-tsuki* (right middle body lunge punch using the normal fist).

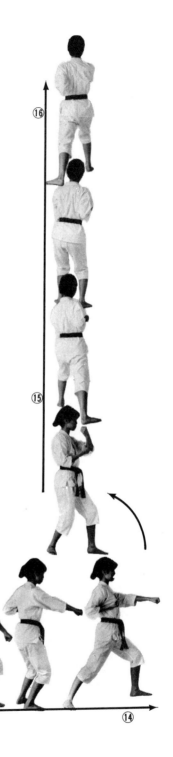

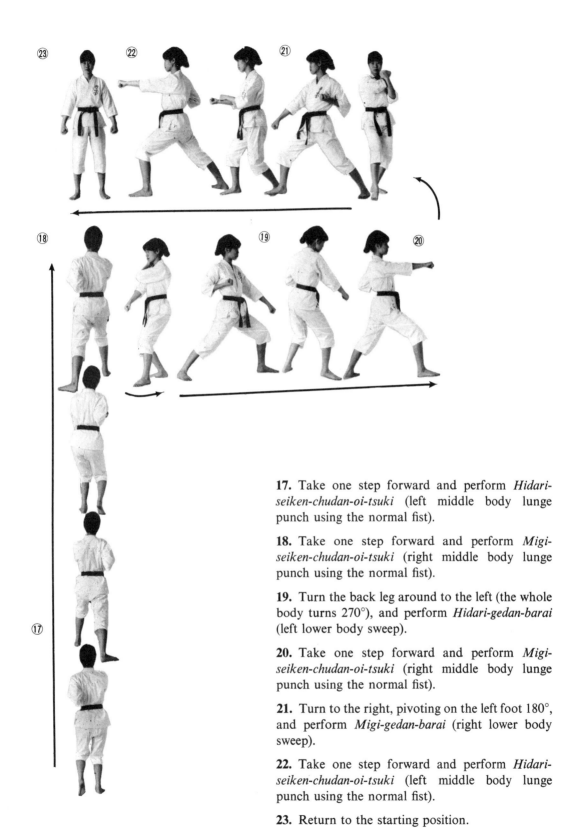

17. Take one step forward and perform *Hidari-seiken-chudan-oi-tsuki* (left middle body lunge punch using the normal fist).

18. Take one step forward and perform *Migi-seiken-chudan-oi-tsuki* (right middle body lunge punch using the normal fist).

19. Turn the back leg around to the left (the whole body turns 270°), and perform *Hidari-gedan-barai* (left lower body sweep).

20. Take one step forward and perform *Migi-seiken-chudan-oi-tsuki* (right middle body lunge punch using the normal fist).

21. Turn to the right, pivoting on the left foot 180°, and perform *Migi-gedan-barai* (right lower body sweep).

22. Take one step forward and perform *Hidari-seiken-chudan-oi-tsuki* (left middle body lunge punch using the normal fist).

23. Return to the starting position.

TAIKYOKU 3

1. Starting position is the same as that of the previous *kata*.

2. Turn to the left and perform the *Hidari-chudan-naka-uke* (left middle body block from inside). Here, you should be in the *Kokutsu-tachi* position (back stance). You will be in this position after each execution of *Naka-uke*.

3. Put the right foot one step forward and perform *Migi-oi-tsuki* (right lunge punch) finishing in *Zenkutsu-tachi* (forward stance). You will be in this stance following every punch.

4. Turn the right arm to the right, making a 180° turn.

5. Perform *Migi-chudan-naka-uke* (right middle body block from the inside). At this time, you should be in the *Kokutsu-tachi* position (back stance) again.

6. Put the left foot one step forward and perform *Hidari-oi-tsuki* (left lunge punch).

7. Turn the left leg 90° to the left, stepping into *Zenkutsu-tachi* (forward stance) and perform *Hidari-gedan-barai* (left lower body sweep).

100

8. Take one step forward and perform *Migi-jodan-oi-tsuki* (right upper body lunge punch).

9. Take one step forward and perform *Hidari-jodan-oi-tsuki* (left upper body lunge punch).

10. Then step forward and perform *Migi-jodan-oi-tsuki* (right upper body lunge punch).

11. Using the right foot as a pivoting foot, turn 270° to the left and perform *Hidari-chudan-naka-uke* (left middle body block from the inside).

12. Take one step forward and perform *Migi-chudan-oi-tsuki* (right middle body lunge punch).

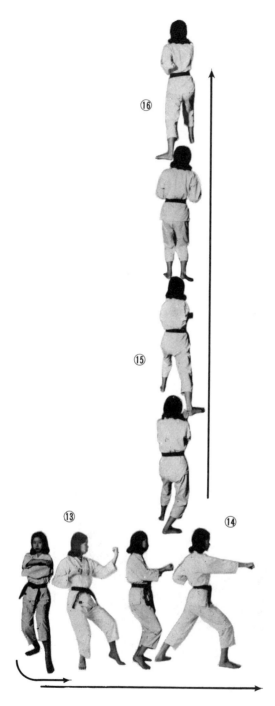

13. Make a 180° turn to the right and perform *Migi-chudan-naka-uke* (right middle body block from the inside).

14. Take one step forward and perform *Hidari-chudan-tsuki* (left middle body thrust).

NOTE: The photographs for steps 13 and 14 show the karateka with her hands and feet in the wrong positions.

15. Make a 90° turn to the left and perform *Hidari-gedan-barai* (left lower body sweep). You should be in *Zenkutsu-tachi* position (forward stance) at this moment.

16. Step forward and perform *Migi-jodan-tsuki* (right upper body thrust).

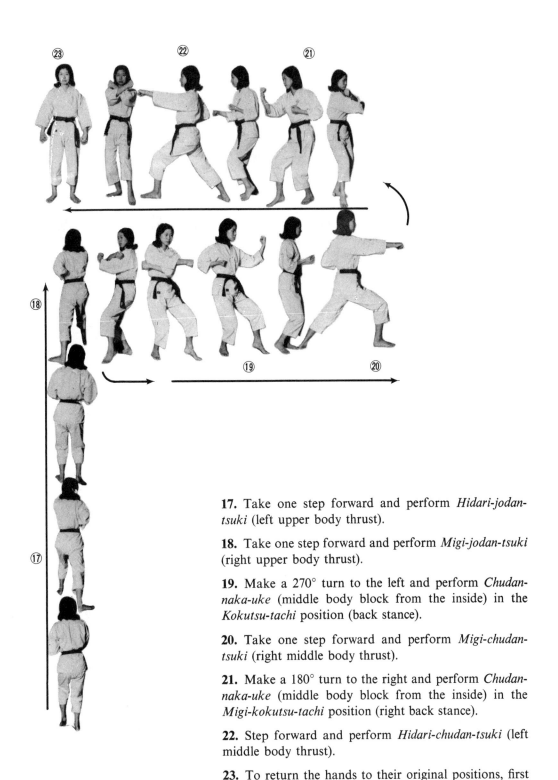

17. Take one step forward and perform *Hidari-jodan-tsuki* (left upper body thrust).

18. Take one step forward and perform *Migi-jodan-tsuki* (right upper body thrust).

19. Make a 270° turn to the left and perform *Chudan-naka-uke* (middle body block from the inside) in the *Kokutsu-tachi* position (back stance).

20. Take one step forward and perform *Migi-chudan-tsuki* (right middle body thrust).

21. Make a 180° turn to the right and perform *Chudan-naka-uke* (middle body block from the inside) in the *Migi-kokutsu-tachi* position (right back stance).

22. Step forward and perform *Hidari-chudan-tsuki* (left middle body thrust).

23. To return the hands to their original positions, first form a cross in front of the chest. Then drop them to the starting position.

HEIAN 4

1. Start by taking the *Fudo-tachi* stance (ready stance).

2. Place the left foot one step to the left while reaching across the body with the left hand and placing it on top of the right one.

3. The left hand now performs *Chudan-tegatana-uke* (middle body handsword block), and the right hand performs *Jodan-tegatana-uke* (upper body handsword block).

4. Bring both hands to the left side of the body with the right hand above the left one while bringing the left foot back towards the right.

5. Place the right foot one step to the right. The right hand performs *Chudan-tegatana-uke* (middle body handsword block) and the left hand performs *Jodan-tegatana-uke* (upper body handsword block). You should now be in the *Kokutsu-tachi* stance (back stance).

6. Take one step forward with the left foot and perform *Gedan-juji-uke* (lower body X-block).

7. Take one step forward with the right foot and perform *Morote-naka-uke* (two-hand block from the inside).

8. Bring the back foot forward and place it next to the front foot. Bring both hands to the right side of the body.

9. Attack the opponent with *Hidari-ashigatana* (left footsword) and *Hidari-uraken* (left back fist) at the same time.

10. As you bring the left foot down, assume the *Zenkutsu-tachi* position (forward stance). The right elbow comes across to the left hand to perform *Hiji-uchi* (elbow thrust). Keep the right hand in *Tettsui* position (iron hammer fist).

11. Bring both feet together; place the right hand above the left one at the left side of the body.

12. Perform *Migi-yoko-geri* (right side kick) and *Migi-uraken* (right back fist).

13. As you bring the right foot down, bring the left elbow across to the right hand using *Hiji-uchi* (elbow thrust). Keep the left hand in *Tettsui* (iron hammer fist).

14. Twist the body around to the left until you are facing forward. The left arm should be stretched out to the front slightly above eye level. The right hand should be on a level with the ear. Continue twisting the body to the left and assume a left forward stance (*Hidari-zenkutsu-tachi*). At this point, the position of the hands should be reversed.

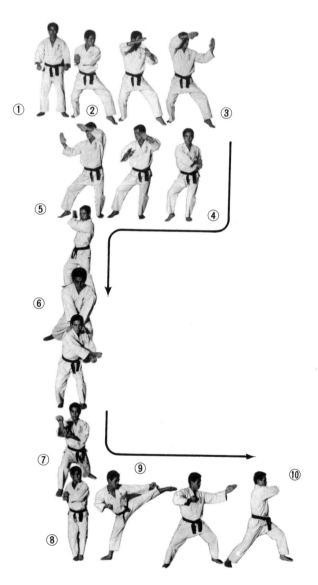

15. Now perform a *Migi-mae-geri* (right front kick).

16. Jump one step to the side and assume *Kake-ashi-tachi* (hooked foot stance), then attack the opponent's face using *Migi-uraken* (right back fist).

17. Place the right foot towards the right side at a 45° angle from the left foot. Cross both hands in front of the chest.

18. Uncross the hands . . .

19. . . . and perform *Migi-mae-geri* (right front kick).

20. As you bring your foot down, step forward and perform *Hidari-seiken-chudan-tsuki* (left middle body thrust with normal fist).

21. Perform *Migi-chudan-tsuki* (right middle body thrust). It is of particular importance that 20 and 21 be performed in rapid succession.

22. Step around with the right foot and bring the right hand to the back at a 45° angle from the middle of the right side and cross both hands in front of the chest.

23. As you uncross the hands . . .

24. . . . perform *Hidari-mae-geri* (left front kick).

25. Bring the left foot down, assume *Zenkutsu-tachi* (forward stance), and perform *Migi-chudan-tsuki* (right middle body thrust).

26. Then, perform *Hidari-chudan-tsuki* (left middle body thrust). It is of particular importance that the right and left hand movements be performed in rapid succession.

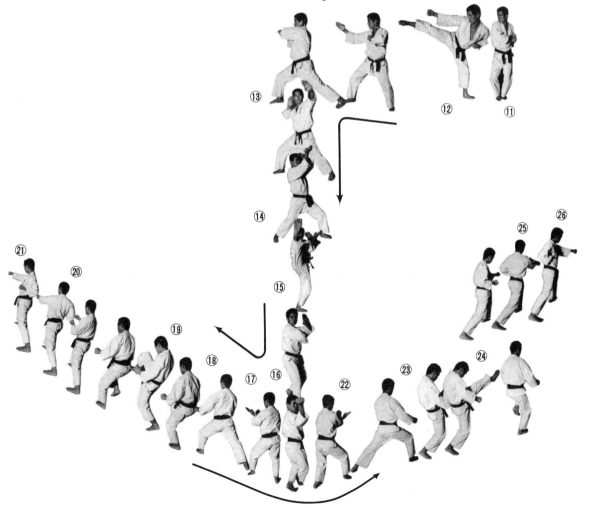

27. As you bring the left foot to the center-line . . .

28. . . . perform *Hidari-chudan-morote-naka-uke* (left middle body two-hand block from the inside).

29. Then, stepping forward with the right foot, perform *Migi-chudan-morote-naka-uke* (right middle body two-hand block from the inside).

30. Step forward with the left foot and perform *Hidari-chudan-morote-naka-uke* (left two-hand middle body block from the inside).

31. Remaining in the same position, raise both hands and attack the opponent by grabbing his hair or neck.

32. Pull down the opponent's head by grabbing his hair, and attack him with *Migi-hiza-geri* (right knee kick).

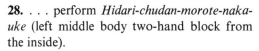

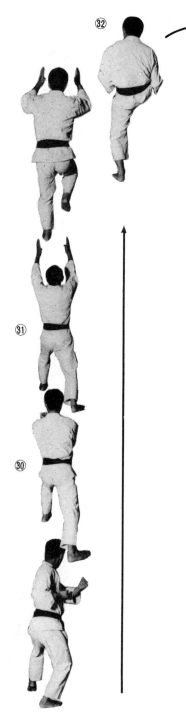

33. As you bring the right foot down, turn to the left.

34. Perform *Hidari-tegatana-uke* (left handsword block).

35. Take one step forward with the right foot and perform *Migi-tegatana-uke* (right handsword block).

36. Return to the original position.

1. Assume the ready stance.

2. Put the left foot one step to the left and assume *Kokutsu-tachi* position (back stance). Bring the left arm to the right side of the body and the right arm to the left side of the body.

3. Remaining in the *Kokutsu-tachi* position, perform *Chudan-naka-uke* with the left hand (middle body block from the inside). At the same time, withdraw the right hand.

4. Perform *Chudan-gyaku-tsuki* (middle body thrust from the reverse position).

5. Bring the right foot close to the left foot, and at the same time, place the left hand on top of the right hand at the right side of the body.

6. Place the right foot one step to the right and bring the right hand towards the left underarm.

7. Assume *Kokutsu-tachi* (back stance) and perform *Migi-chudan-naka-uke* (right middle body block from the inside).

8. Remaining in the same position, perform *Hidari-chudan-tsuki* (left middle body thrust).

9. Bring the left foot next to the right foot and put both hands together at the left side of the body.

10. Take one step forward with the right foot and assume *Zenkutsu-tachi* position (forward stance) while performing *Migi-chudan-morote-naka-uke* (right middle body two-hand block from the inside).

11. Take one step forward with the left foot bringing both hands up to the right side of the head and perform *Gedan-juji-uke* (lower body X-block).

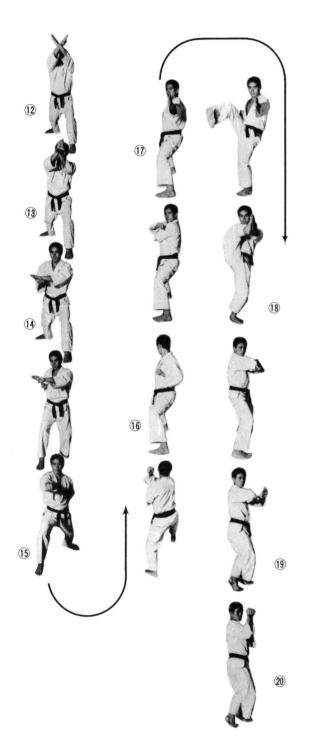

12. Then, quickly, raise both hands and perform *Juji-ue-uke* (X-block from below).

13. Gradually lower the hands, and at the same time rotate the left wrist until the left palm is facing up.

14. The hands should be on a level with the chest at the right side of the body with the wrists touching.

15. Take one step forward with the right foot and perform *Migi-chudan-tsuki* (right middle body thrust).

16. Turn the right leg around to the back and assume *Kiba-tachi* position (horse stance), and perform *Gedan-barai* (lower body sweep).

17. Remaining in *Kiba-tachi* (horse stance), cross the arms in front of the chest, and then stretch out the right arm to the right and the left arm to the left.

18. Touch the palm of the left hand with the *Soko-ashi* (arch of the foot) of the right foot, then quickly assume *Kiba-tachi* (horse stance) again.

19. As you take the *Kake-ashi-tachi* position (hooked foot stance), get ready to strike an opponent with the *Migi-uraken* (right back fist).

20. Attack the opponent with *Migi-uraken* (right back fist) and *Hidari-shotei* (left palm heel thrust).

21. Place the left leg one step to the left side and raise the right arm.

22. Jump into the air and shout a forceful, *Kiai!* (*Kiai* is the traditional Japanese term shouted when performing an attack). While in the air, bend both legs at the knee and perform *Gedan-juji-uke* (lower body X-block) with both hands.

23. As you land, assume the *Zenkutsu-tachi* (forward stance) with the right leg in front. Then perform *Migi-naka-uke* (right hand block from the inside).

24. Drop the back leg (left leg) farther to the back in order to widen the stance. Cross the left arm in front of the chest so that the left hand is beside the right ear. The right arm crosses beneath the left arm and the right hand shields the lower body. Bend the left knee to lower the stance. The right hand may be used to grab an opponent by the ankle in order to trip him.

25. The right arm is raised to the side. The karateka is now in a horse stance and performing *Gedan-barai* (lower body sweep) with the left hand.

26. Bring the right foot over to the left one so that both heels are touching.

27. Then, step forward with the right foot at a 45° angle assuming the *Kiba-tachi* (horse stance). Cross the right arm in front of the chest so that the right hand is beside the left ear. The left arm crosses beneath the right arm and the left hand protects the lower body.

28. Bend the right knee to lower the stance. The left hand is used to grab an opponent by the ankle in order to trip him. Reassume the *Kiba-tachi* and perform *Gedan-barai* (lower body sweep) with the right hand. The left arm is raised to the side.

29. Bring the right leg back to the original position and assume the *Fudo-tachi* (ready stance).

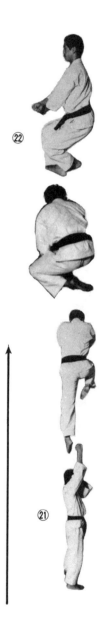

SAIHA

1. Assume ready stance.

2. Assume the *Musubi-tachi* (linked foot stance) and meditate.

3. Cross the arms in front of the chest so that the right hand is beside the left ear and the left hand is beside the the right ear. Gradually open the arms and assume the *Fudo-tachi* (ready stance).

4. Place the right foot diagonally one step forward making a 45° angle with the body.

5. Bring the left foot over to the right foot and assume the *Musubi-tachi* (linked foot stance). At the same time, bring the right hand up to the armpit and place the left hand over it.

6. Attack the opponent's jaw with the right elbow.

7. Place the left foot one step to the side and assume the *Han-kiba-tachi* (half horse stance). Attack the opponent's face using *Uraken* (back fist) and at the same time shield the solar plexus with the left hand using the *Shotei* (palm heel).

8. Place the left foot diagonally one step forward to make a 45° angle with the body.

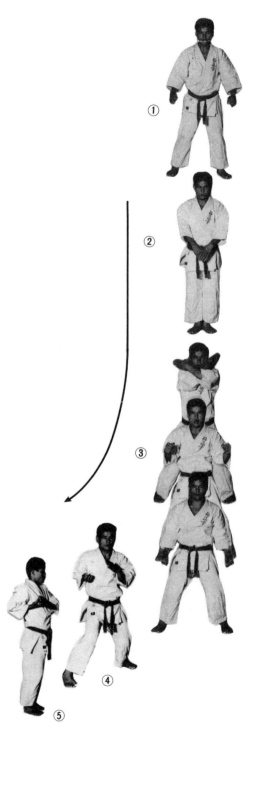

9. Bring the right foot over to the left foot and assume the *Musubi-tachi* (linked foot stance). At the same time, bring the left hand to the armpit and place the right hand over it.

10. Attack the opponent's jaw with the left elbow.

11. Place the right foot one step to the side and assume the *Han-kiba-tachi* (half horse stance). Attack the opponent's face using *Uraken* (back fist) and at the same time shield the solar plexus with the right hand with *Shotei* (palm heel).

12. Place the right foot diagonally one step forward to form a 45° angle with the body.

13. Bring the left foot over to the right one and assume the *Musubi-tachi* (linked foot stance). At the same time, bring the right hand over to the right armpit and place the left hand over it.

14. Attack the opponent's jaw with the right elbow.

15. Place the left foot one step to the side and assume the *Han-kiba-tachi* (half horse stance). Attack the opponent's face with *Uraken* (back fist) using the right hand and protect the spleen area with the left hand.

16. Bring the left foot over to the right foot and assume the *Neko-ashi-tachi* (cat stance).

17. Perform *Ue-uke* (block from below) using *Hidari-shotei* (left palm heel thrust) and then *Shita-uke* (block from above) using *Migi-shotei* (right palm heel thrust).

18. Perform *Migi-mae-geri* (right front kick).

19. After kicking, bring the leg down to the previous position. Then, place the right foot one step to the side.

20. Bring the left foot over to the right foot, making the *Neko-ashi-tachi* (cat stance). Perform *Ue-uke* (rising block) using the right palm heel thrust and perform *Shita-uke* (block from above) using the left palm heel.

21. Perform *Hidari-mae-geri* (left front kick).

22. Bring the left foot to the back and assume the *Migi-zenkutsu-tachi* (right forward stance).

23. Cross the arms in front of the body, pull the stretched arms back to the armpits . . .

24. . . . and then thrust both arms out and perform *Seiken-jodan-morote-tsuki* (upper body thrust with both hands in normal fists).

25. Open the arms out to the sides and lower them using a large circular motion. Then, place the left hand in *Shotei* (palm heel thrust) and the right hand in *Tettsui* (iron hammer fist), and bring them together tightly in front of you at waist level.

26. Bring the right foot one step to the left side and turn.

27. Cross the arms in front of the body in order to form *Juji-uke* (X-block), then pull them back towards the armpits to create the momentum needed for performing *Seiken-morote-tsuki* (thrust using both hands in the normal fist). The karateka is in *Hidari-zenkutsu-tachi* (left forward stance).

28. Open both arms and lower them using a large circular motion. Then, place the right hand in *Shotei* (palm heel thrust) and the left hand in *Tettsui* (iron hammer fist), and bring them together at waist level.

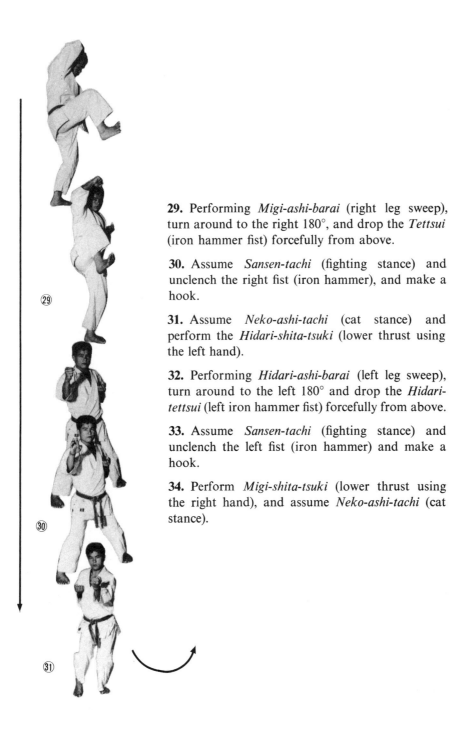

29. Performing *Migi-ashi-barai* (right leg sweep), turn around to the right 180°, and drop the *Tettsui* (iron hammer fist) forcefully from above.

30. Assume *Sansen-tachi* (fighting stance) and unclench the right fist (iron hammer), and make a hook.

31. Assume *Neko-ashi-tachi* (cat stance) and perform the *Hidari-shita-tsuki* (lower thrust using the left hand).

32. Performing *Hidari-ashi-barai* (left leg sweep), turn around to the left 180° and drop the *Hidari-tettsui* (left iron hammer fist) forcefully from above.

33. Assume *Sansen-tachi* (fighting stance) and unclench the left fist (iron hammer) and make a hook.

34. Perform *Migi-shita-tsuki* (lower thrust using the right hand), and assume *Neko-ashi-tachi* (cat stance).

35. Place the right foot one step forward and assume *Sansen-tachi* (fighting stance), and at the same time, perform *Hidari-seiken-tsuki* (thrust using the left normal fist).

36. Turn 180° to the right. Using a circular motion, bring the right forearm in *Kake* (hook) manner in front of the forehead.

37. Perform a *Hidari-mawashi-uke* (left roundhouse block) and assume the *Neko-ashi-tachi* (cat stance).

38. The left hand performs *Jodan-uke* (upper body block) and the right hand performs *Gedan-uke* (lower body block).

39. Now practice the *Ibuki* (breathing exercise described on page 82). Bring the right foot over to the left foot and assume *Musubi-tachi* (linked foot stance). Clasp the hands in front of the body with the left hand on top (palms should be facing the body). Bring the arms up to the level of the face and rotate the hands 180° without separating them so that they are in the same position as when you started, but reversed. Gradually lower the hands and relax the body in order to calm the heavy breathing.

40. Return to the original position.

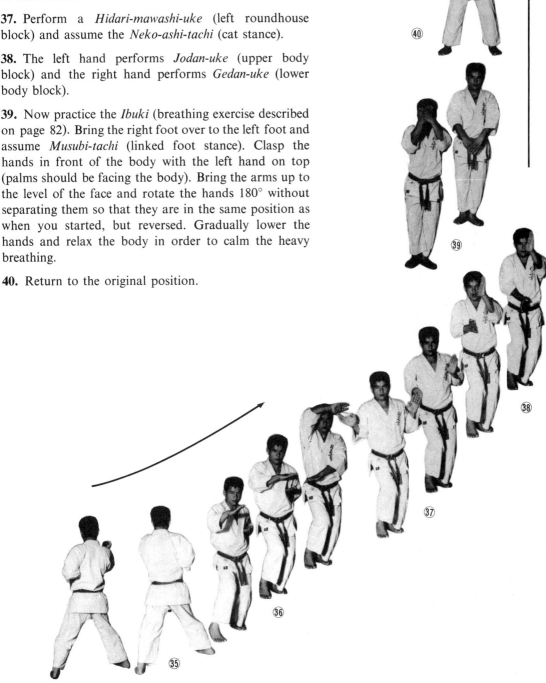

4. Kumite (Sparring)

第五章　組手

All of the martial arts are involved with fighting, so, of course, the techniques of karate presuppose combat. However, the karateka should understand that karate was meant to *prevent* fights, not cause them, and should therefore use it only as a deterrent.

Up to now, you have been learning the basic exercises, forms and techniques, but still have yet to get the feeling of true karate. It is time now to learn the techniques of *kumite* (sparring) with an actual opponent.

You, the karateka, must realize that you are embarking now upon the most difficult phase of training and must be able to focus your concentration on many aspects at the same time. For instance, you must always be aware of the most minute details concerning your opponent; his breathing pattern, his style of attack and defense, his balance, his speed, and the times when he is the most vulnerable. Of course, at the same time you must be concentrating on your own fight plan.

Once again, I re-emphasize the importance of using karate correctly. Once you learn through sparring of the power of karate, you will understand why its indiscriminate use can be fatal. Sparring will give you a healthy respect for the sport of karate and will test how well you have mastered your lessons up to now.

Side view of Morote

PREPARATORY TECHNIQUES FOR JIYU-KUMITE (FREE SPARRING)

The first important point is that when sparring you never actually hit the opponent. Rather, stop your blow just short of the opponent's *Gi* (traditional karate outfit). Secondly, always have an instructor present whenever practicing *kumite* (sparring).

Many schools of karate recommend using the *Kiba-tachi* (horse stance), *Sansen-tachi* (fighting stance), and *Shiko-tachi* (Sumo stance) as the preliminary *kumite* stances. However, these stances tend to be rather clumsy and less stable—it is easy to get tripped up when using these stances. As a rule, any stance chosen as a preliminary should be one in which the feet are shoulder-width apart and perpendicular to each other.

1. Preparatory stance using Morote (both hands)

Clench both fists, put the left foot one step forward and assume either *Neko-ashi-tachi* (cat stance) or *Kokutsu-tachi* (back stance). The left hand is stretched forward to block upper body thrusts and the right arm is used to sweep aside the kicking leg of an opponent. In general, this type of closed-arm stance is safer and less vulnerable than an open-arm stance.

2. Preparatory stance using Enshin (center of the circle or pinwheel)

Assume either *Neko-ashi-tachi* (cat stance) or *Kokutsu-tachi* (back stance) position. Put the left arm forward at eye level, and keep the right arm at waist level either in *Shotei* (palm heel) or *Tegatana* (handsword) position. *Enshin* (pinwheel) gets its name from the way you constantly rotate your hands in a circular motion in order to confuse an opponent.

Front view of preparatory stance using Morote

Front view

Preparatory stance using Enshin

120

Side view of Ryuhen **Front view of Ryuhen**

3. Preparatory stance using Ryuhen (moving dragon stance)

Assume either *Neko-ashi-tachi* (cat stance) or *Kokutsu-tachi* (back stance). Bend the arms in front of the chest parallel to each other and separated by several inches. Then, put the left foot one step forward and assume *Neko-ashi-tachi* (cat stance). The lower hand blocks the lower body thrusts and the upper hand blocks the upper body thrusts. Repeat over and over. This constant movement of the arms is used to confuse and overwhelm the opponent.

4. Preparatory stance using Maeba (front part of the wing)

Assume either *Neko-ashi-tachi* (cat stance) or *Moro-ashi-tachi* (two foot stance). Both arms are stretched forward as if to ward off an attack. This is also a useful means of measuring the distance between

Front view of Maeba

121

Side view of Maeba

you and the opponent, at the same time leaving you room with which to perform kicking manoeuvres. This technique is based on observations of predatory birds which use the front part of their wings to render their prey unconscious prior to carrying them off.

5. Preparatory stance using Birin (tail of dragon stance)

The right arm is stretched forward in *Nukite* position (piercing hand) and the left hand crosses over in front of the chest so that the left hand is directly below the right elbow (the left hand should be palm down). The karateka should assume the *Neko-ashi-tachi* (cat stance). The lower hand blocks kicks such as *Kinteki-geri* (testicle kick), *Mae-geri* (front kick), and *Mawashi-geri* (roundhouse kick), and the upper hand blocks the upper body thrusts. Both hands are also used for attacking, using the motions of a dragon's tail.

NOTE: Stances which are most often used include *Kiba-tachi* (horse stance), *Moro-ashi-tachi* (two foot stance), *Kokutsu-tachi* (back stance) and *Neko-ashi-tachi* (cat stance): however, the single most effective stance is the *Neko-ashi-tachi* because of its great stability and adaptability.

Side view of Birin

Front view of Birin

MA-AI (TIME AND SPACE RELATIONSHIP)

In karate, *Ma-ai* is a combination of the distance between you and your opponent and the speed of movement that each possesses. Other influencing factors are size of the participants and each opponent's fighting style. The optimum distance for the *Ma-ai* is obviously different for each karateka; however, there must be space enough for unrestricted offense or defense.

So-ou-ma-ai (one step)

This is the closest you can get to your opponent and still maintain control.

So-ou-ma-ai

Yudo-ma-ai (one and a half steps)

This is a median distance *Ma-ai*. By taking the extra half step backwards, you induce your opponent to step closer and possibly fall into a planned trap.

Yudo-ma-ai

Gendo-ma-ai (two steps)

This is a maximum controllable distance between two participants, By taking an extra step backwards from the *So-ou-ma-ai,* the karateka gives himself a moment with which to plan his next move.

Gendo-ma-ai

It is of utmost importance that you constantly think about the *Ma-ai* as all of the techniques in this book have been designed for the utmost effectiveness in practice. Indiscriminate or unthinking attacks will only lead to wasted movement and possibly loss of the fight.

As you become experienced at *kumite* (sparring), you will appreciate the advantages of the *Ma-ai* more and more. For example, the extra step can make the difference between a blow thrown with momentum and one thrown without momentum. Also, the extra distance gives you a chance to observe an opponent's weaknesses and vulnerabilities.

When fully experienced, the karateka alternates between the three types of *Ma-ai* as the situation demands. For example, if you call *So-ou-ma-ai* "A," *Yudo-ma-ai* "B," and *Gendo-ma-ai* "C," you can combine the three as, for example, A-C-B-A-B-C-C-A-C-B.

You must constantly practice such variations in order to integrate them smoothly into every sparring routine.

SANBON-KUMITE (THREE FORM SPARRING)

Sanbon-kumite is the bridge between the basic principles that you have learned up to now and the advanced free style sparring (*Jiyu-kumite*) which you will learn of shortly.

In *Sanbon-kumite,* one karateka is the attacker and one is the blocker. The attacker performs three consecutive attack forms (blows, kicks or any combination) and the blocker performs three blocks against these attacks. Each offensive blow should be performed while moving forward. At the conclusion of each three-part form, the two participants change rôles and continue in the reverse direction.

In the following photos, in order to make it easier to follow the movements, the attacker is wearing black *Gi,* and the blocker is wearing white *Gi.*

1. Sanbon-kumite using only the arms and hands

A-1. The participants respectfully bow to each other.

A-2. The participants are preparing for first contact. Black is in *Gedan-barai* (lower body sweep) and White is in either *Han-heiko-tachi* (half parallel stance) or *Fudo-tachi* (ready stance).

NOTE: These first two (1-2) preliminary forms should be performed prior to all *kumite.*

A-3. Black performs *Oi-tsuki* (lunge punch) and White blocks it with *Hidari-chudan-naka-uke* (left middle body block from the inside). White puts his right foot one step backwards.

A-4. Black performs *Oi-tsuki* again and White blocks it with *Migi-chudan-naka-uke* (right middle body block from the inside) this time. White places the left foot one step backwards.

A-5. Same as A-3.

A-6. As soon as White performs the block, he steps forward and performs *Chudan-seiken-tsuki* (middle body thrust using normal fist).

B-1. The bow and the preparation are the same as A-1 and A-2. White blocks Black's *Migi-seiken-tsuki* (right thrust using the normal fist) with *Migi-chudan-uke* (right middle body block).

B-2. Black performs *Hidari-seiken-oi-tsuki* (left lunge punch using normal fist) and White blocks it with *Hidari-chudan-naka-uke* (left middle body block from the inside).

B-3. Same as B-1.

B-4. As soon as White blocks Black's attack, he steps forward and attacks Black's rib cage and abdominal area with *Hidari-seiken-tsuki* (left thrust using the normal fist).

C-1. The bow and the preparation are the same as A-1 and A-2. Black performs *Chudan-oi-tsuki* (middle body lunge punch) and White blocks it with *Chudan-soto-uke* (middle body block from the outside). The position of the feet is the same as in A-3.

C-2. Black performs *Hidari-chudan-oi-tsuki* (left middle body lunge punch) and White blocks it with *Migi-soto-uke* (right block from the outside).

C-3. Same as C-1.

C-4. Immediately after blocking Black's attack, White steps forward and attacks the opponent's rib cage with *Migi-seiken-gyaku-tsuki* (right thrust in a reverse manner using the normal fist).

D-1. The beginning is the same as the previous ones. Black performs *Hidari-seiken-tsuki* (left thrust using the normal fist) and White defends himself with *Soto-uke* (block from the outside).

D-2. White blocks Black's right attack with *Migi-soto-uke* (right block from the outside).

126

D — 3

D — 4

E — 1

E — 2

E — 3

E — 4

D-3. Same as D-1.

D-4. Immediately after sweeping away Black's attack White attacks to the face or stomach.

E-1. The beginning is the same as before. White blocks Black's *Migi-chudan-oi-tsuki* (right middle body lunge punch) with *Hidari-chudan-barai-oroshi* (left middle body sweeping drop).

E-2. White blocks Black's *Hidari-chudan-oi-tsuki* (left middle body lunge punch) with *Migi-chudan-barai-oroshi* (right middle body sweeping drop).

E-3. Same as E-1.

E-4. At the same time that White sweeps away Black's attack, he steps forward and attacks the opponent's stomach.

F — 1

F — 2

F — 3

F — 4

F-1. The beginning is the same as before. Black performs *Migi-jodan-tsuki* (right upper body thrust) and White blocks it with *Hidari-jodan-uke* (left upper body block).

F-2. Black performs *Hidari-jodan-tsuki* (left upper body thrust) and White puts his left foot one step backwards and blocks it with *Migi-jodan-uke* (right upper body block).

F-3. Same as F-1.

F-4. Turning the left arm (blocking arm) outwards, White lowers Black's attacking arm and attacks Black's face with his right fist.

G-1. The beginning is the same as before. White blocks Black's *Migi-jodan-tsuki* (right upper body thrust) with *Migi-jodan-uke* (right upper body block) to the inside.

G-2. Black performs *Hidari-jodan-tsuki* (left upper body thrust) and White blocks it with *Hidari-jodan-uke* (left upper body block), and puts his right foot one step backwards.

G-3. Same as G-1.

G-4. As White blocks Black's thrust with *Migi-jodan-uke* (right upper body block), he steps forward and attacks the opponent's rib cage with *Tettsui* (iron hammer fist) using the hand which was used for blocking.

H-1. Black performs *Migi-chudan-tsuki* (right middle body thrust) and White blocks it with *Migi-shotei-uke* (right palm heel block), and puts the left foot one step backwards. Here, White is in *Zenkutsu-tachi* position (forward stance).

H-2. Black performs *Hidari-chudan-tsuki* (left middle body thrust) and White blocks it with *Hidari-shotei-uke* (left palm heel block), and puts the right foot one step backwards.

H-3. Same as H-1.

H-4. White blocks Black's *Migi-chudan-tsuki* (right middle body thrust) with *Migi-shotei-uke* (right palm heel block), then attacks the opponent's jaw with *Migi-tegatana* (right handsword).

G—1

H—1

G—2

H—2

G—3

H—3

G—4

H—4

I — 1

I — 2

I — 3

I — 4

J — 1

J — 2

J — 3

J — 4

K — 1

K — 2

K — 3

K — 4

I-1. Black performs *Migi-chudan-tsuki* (right middle body thrust). White puts his left foot one step backwards assuming *Zenkutsu-tachi* (forward stance) and blocks it with *Migi-chudan-soto-uke* (right middle body block from the outside).

I-2. White blocks Black's *Hidari-chudan-tsuki* (left middle body thrust) with *Chudan-soto-uke* (middle body block from the outside), putting his right foot one step backwards assuming *Zenkutsu-tachi* (forward stance).

I-3. Same as I-1.

I-4. Using the blocking hand (right hand), White attacks the opponent's face with *Uraken* (back fist).

J-1. Beginning as before. Black performs *Migi-chudan-oi-tsuki* (right middle body lunge punch) and White blocks it with *Hidari-shotei-soto-uke* (left palm heel block from the outside). White withdraws his right foot while blocking and assumes the *Kiba-tachi* (horse stance).

J-2. White blocks Black's *Hidari-chudan-tsuki* (left middle body thrust) with *Migi-shotei* (right palm heel), and withdraws his left foot while blocking and assumes the horse stance.

J-3. Same as in J-1. The right hand should be ready to attack.

J-4. White attacks the opponent's spleen area with *Migi-segatana* (right reverse handsword).

K-1. White blocks Black's *Migi-chudan-tsuki* (right middle body thrust) with *Migi-tegatana-uke* (right handsword block). In this case, White hits the opponent's wrist as he blocks. White should be in *Neko-ashi-tachi* (cat stance); however, during exercises he could as well be in either *Zenkutsu-tachi* (forward stance) or *Kokutsu-tachi* (back stance).

K-2. White blocks Black's *Hidari-chudan-tsuki* (left middle body thrust) with *Hidari-tegatana* (left handsword) and puts his right foot one step backwards.

K-3. Same as K-1.

K-4. Turning the blocking hand, White steps forward and hits the opponent's rib cage with *Hidari-tegatana* (left handsword).

L-1. White blocks Black's *Migi-chudan-oi-tsuki* (right middle body lunge punch) with *Hidari-tegatana-uke* (left handsword block) and puts his right foot one step backwards and assumes *Neko-ashi-tachi* (cat stance).

L-2. White blocks Black's *Hidari-chudan-tsuki* (left middle body thrust) with *Migi-tegatana-uke* (right handsword block), and withdraws his left foot and assumes *Neko-ashi-tachi* (cat stance).

L-3. Same as L-1.

L-4. Pushing down the opponent's right hand with his left hand, White attacks the opponent's neck with *Tegatana* (handsword). At the same time, White steps forward and assumes *Zenkutsu-tachi* (forward stance).

M-1. Black performs *Migi-chudan-tsuki* (right middle body thrust) and White blocks it with *Hidari-segatana-naka-uke* (left block from inside using reverse handsword), and assumes *Neko-ashi-tachi* (cat stance) with his left foot in front.

M-2. White blocks Black's *Hidari-chudan-tsuki* (left middle body thrust) with *Migi-segatana-naka-uke* (right block from the inside using the reverse handsword), and assumes *Neko-ashi-tachi* (cat stance) with the right foot in front.

M-3. Same as M-1.

M-4. As White blocks Black's attack, he strikes Black's jaw with *Migi-shotei* (right palm heel).

N-1. White blocks Black's *Migi-chudan-tsuki* (right middle body thrust) with *Shotei-oroshi-uke* (palm heel drop block), and assumes *Neko-ashi-tachi* (cat stance) with the left foot in front.

N-2. White blocks Black's *Hidari-chudan-tsuki* (left middle body thrust) with *Migi-shotei-oroshi-uke* (right palm heel drop block) and assumes *Neko-ashi-tachi* (cat stance) with the right foot in front.

N-3. Same as N-1.

N-4. Sweeping away Black's thrust, White strikes Black's face with *Migi-nukite* (right piercing hand).

M — 1

M — 2

M — 3

M — 4

N — 1

N — 2

N — 3

N — 4

2. Sanbon-kumite using legs as attacking weapons

You must never forget that the *kumite* always begins with a bow and ends with a bow.

A-1. Black performs *Migi-mae-geri* (front kick using the right leg) and White withdraws his right foot one step while at the same time he performs *Hidari-gedan-barai* (left lower body sweep).

A-2. White places his left foot one step backwards and at the same time, he performs *Migi-gedan-barai* (right lower body sweep) against Black's *Hidari-mae-geri* (front kick using the left leg).

A-3. Same as A-1.

A-4. Sweeping away Black's right leg, White strikes Black's solar plexus with *Migi-seiken-gyaku-tsuki* (right normal fist thrust in a reverse manner).

B-1. White blocks Black's *Migi-mae-geri* (front kick using the right foot) with *Migi-soto-gedan-barai* (right lower body sweep from the outside).

B-2. White blocks Black's *Hidari-mae-geri* (front kick using the left foot) with *Hidari-soto-gedan-barai* (left lower body sweep from the outside) as he withdraws his right foot one step.

B-3. Same as B-1.

B-4. As White sweeps away Black's kicking leg, he pushes it around so that he can strike Black's spinal area from behind.

C-1. White blocks Black's *Migi-mawashi-geri* (right roundhouse kick) with *Chudan-soto-uke* (middle body block from the outside). He is then in *Kiba-tachi* (horse stance).

C-2. White blocks Black's *Hidari-mawashi-geri* (left roundhouse kick) with *Hidari-soto-uke* (left block from the outside). The stance is the same as in C-1.

C-3. This is the same as C-1.

C-4. As White sweeps away Black's kicking leg, he strikes the opponent's jaw using *Tettsui* (iron hammer fist).

D-1. Black performs *Yoko-geri-age* (upper side kick) and White blocks it with *Hidari-chudan-uke* (left middle body block).

D-2. White blocks Black's *Yoko-geri-age* (upper side kick) with *Migi-chudan-uke* (right middle body block). Although the blocking is done with middle body blocks here, it should vary from lower body to upper body depending upon the height of the kicks.

D-3. Same as D-1.

D-4. As White pushes away the ankle of Black's kicking leg, he turns Black's body around and at the same time steps forward. Then, he kicks Black's left leg joint using *Migi-kansetsu-geri* (right kick to the knee).

E－1

E－2

E－3

E－4

E-1. Black performs *Mae-geri* (front kick). White withdraws his right leg one step, and performs *Hidari-shotei-uke* (left palm heel block).

E-2. White blocks *Hidari-mae-geri* (front kick with left leg) using *Migi-shotei-uk*e (right palm heel block). The left foot is drawn back.

E-3. Same as E-1.

E-4. White grabs Black's kicking leg with both hands and pushes him down.

F－1

F－2

F－3

F－4

F-1. White blocks Black's front kick with his left leg. Whenever you block a kick or a punch, it is most effective if you *push* the striking limb at the same time.

F-2. White blocks Black's *Hidari-mae-geri* (left front kick) with the right knee.

F-3. White blocks Black's *Migi-mae-geri* (right front kick) with the left knee.

F-4. White pushes away Black's kicking leg and at the same time, he kicks Black's jaw using the same leg he used for blocking.

G-1. White blocks Black's *Migi-mae-geri* (right front kick) with *Migi-soko-ashi-uke* (right arch of the foot block).

G-2. White blocks Black's *Hidari-mae-geri* (left front kick) with *Hidari-soko-ashi-uke* (left arch of the foot block).

G-3. Same as G-1.

G-4. As White blocks Black's kick, he knocks Black down with *Yoko-geri* (side kick).

IPPON-KUMITE
(ONE FORM SPARRING)

Ippon-kumite is the final group of exercises before the karateka begins free sparring. In this section, we emphasize single attacks and defenses. It is the combination of these *Ippon-kumite* that will prepare you for *Jiyu-kumite* (free sparring). Emphasis is placed on each technique's individuality; you can no longer depend upon routines containing many related forms, since in free sparring an opponent's moves are generally unexpected. For performing blocks, it is best to stand in *Han-kiba-tachi* (half horse stance). The photos above show (1) two participants facing each other before a contest; (2) the two bow to each other. As stated before, the bow is very important in karate. It shows respect towards the other person, and this is the essential difference between the martial arts and street fighting.

A-1. Two participants are ready. The attacker is on the left throughout.

A-2. One performs *Migi-jodan-tsuki* (right upper body thrust) and the other blocks it with his left hand.

A-3. Turning the blocking hand around and sweeping away the opponent's striking hand, he strikes the opponent's face with *Migi-tegatana* (right handsword).

B-1. The preparatory positions are the same as in A-1. One performs *Jodan-tsuki* (upper body thrust) and the other blocks it with *Migi-jodan-tegatana* (right upper body handsword).

B-2. As he blocks the thrust, he steps forward and strikes the opponent's rib area with *Tegatana* (handsword).

C-1. The beginning is the same as A-1. One performs middle body thrust and the other blocks it with his left hand from the outside.

C-2. Immediately after blocking, he withdraws his left hand and strikes the opponent's knee joint using his right hand. Or, something like B-2 could be performed.

D-1. The beginning is the same as A-1. One performs middle body thrust, and the opponent blocks it with *Hidari-naka-segatana* (left reverse handsword from the inside).

D-2. He withdraws his blocking hand and at the same time, he strikes the opponent's clavicle using *Migi-tegatana* (right handsword).

E-1. Two participants get ready.

E-2. One performs middle body thrust and the other sweeps it away with *Hidari-tegatana* (left handsword).

E-3. Then, he strikes the opponent's stomach area using *Shotei* (palm heel thrust).

F-1. The beginning is the same as E-1. One performs middle body thrust and the other blocks it with *Hidari-soto-shotei-uke* (left palm heel block from the outside).

F-2. Then he steps forward and kicks the back of the opponent's knee joint using his right leg.

G-1. The beginning is the same as E-1. After blocking the opponent's middle body thrust with *Hidari-tegatana-oroshi* (left handsword drop block) from the inside . . .

G-2. . . . he sweeps the thrusting hand away, and at the same time, kicks the opponent's stomach area with *Migi-mae-geri* (right front kick).

H-1. The beginning is the same as E-1. One blocks the opponent's middle body thrust with *Soto-shotei-uke* (palm heel block from the outside).

H-2. At the same time, he kicks the opponent's back part of the thigh using his left shin. This is a very effective technique and the person hit usually cannot stand after being kicked in this manner.

I — 1

I — 2

I-1. Two participants are ready.

I-2. After blocking the opponent's right upper body thrust with *Hidari-jodan-tegatana-uke* (left upper body handsword block) . . .

I — 3

I-3. . . . he turns the striking hand around and pulls it towards him using *Tegatana-kake* (handsword hook). Then, he kicks the opponent's solar plexus area with *Migi-hiza-geri* (right knee kick).

J-1. The beginning is the same as I-1. One blocks *Migi-jodan-tsuki* (right upper body thrust) with *Migi-jodan-uke* (right upper body block).

J-2. He then performs *Mawashi-kake* (roundhouse hook or turning hook) with his blocking hand, and kicks the opponent's right rib area using the left shin. NOTE: Since this technique is very powerful, you must be very careful when using it.

J — 1

J — 2

K-1. The beginning is the same as I-1. One performs *Migi-jodan-tsuki* (right upper body thrust) and the other raises both arms up and sweeps the opponent's striking arm away to the left side. At the same time, he grabs the opponent's head.

K-2. Bringing the opponent's head downwards, he kicks the opponent's face with *Migi-hiza-geri-age* (rising right knee kick).

L-1. The beginning is the same as I-1. Instead of blocking the opponent's right upper body thrust, he lowers his hips and dodges out of the way.

L-2. Grabbing the opponent's testicles, he jumps in and strikes the opponent's rib cage with his head.

M — 1

M-1. Two participants are ready.

M-2. One blocks the opponent's middle body thrust with *Koken* (arc fist) from the inside.

M-3. Then he steps forward with his right foot and strikes the opponent's jaw with *Migi-koken* (right arc fist).

N-1. The beginning is the same as M-1. One blocks the right upper body thrust with *Hidari-koken-age-uke* (left arc fist rising block).

N-2. As he blocks, he places his right foot one step forward and strikes the opponent's rib cage using *Migi-koken* (right arc fist).

M — 2

M — 3

N — 1

N — 2

O-1. The beginning is the same as M-1. One blocks the opponent's right upper body thrust with *Hidari-jodan-tegatana-uke* (left upper body handsword block).

O-2. Turning the blocking hand outwards, he kicks the opponent's jaw with *Migi-mawashi-geri* (right roundhouse kick).

P-1. The beginning is the same as M-1. Instead of blocking the upper body thrust, one lowers his body by dropping his hips in order to avoid the thrust.

P-2. Placing both hands on the floor for support, he kicks the opponent's stomach area with *Migi-mawashi-geri* (right roundhouse kick).

Q — 1

Q-1. The two participants are ready.

Q-2. One blocks the opponent's upper body thrust using *Hidari-tegatana-uke* (left handsword block), then reaches under the opponent's striking arm with his right arm. He then clasps his hands together, thereby imprisoning the opponent's arm.

Q-3. He forces the opponent backwards by pushing against his trapped arm and kicking his right leg out from under him.

R-1. The beginning is the same as Q-1. One blocks the opponent's upper body thrust with *Hidari-tegatana-uke* (left handsword block) and at the same time, he tries to get to the right side of the opponent.

R-2. He grabs the opponent's right leg with his right hand and pushes the opponent's knee joint with his left forearm in order to make him fall.

Q — 2

R — 1

Q — 3

R — 2

S-1. From the preparatory position seen in Q-1, one blocks the opponent's right upper body thrust with a left handsword and turns it outwards.

S-2. He then grabs the opponent by the right leg and pulls it, and at the same time, his left arm pushes the opponent down.

T — 1

T-1. Two participants bowing to each other.

T-2. The two are ready to spar.

T — 2

T-3. One blocks the opponent's upper body thrust with *Ashigatana-yoko-geri-age* (rising side kick using footsword).

T — 4

T-4. He then kicks the opponent's side using the blocking leg in *Ashigatana* position (footsword).

U-1. The beginning is the same as T-1 and T-2. One blocks the opponent's middle body thrust with *Mawashi-soko-ashi-uke* (roundhouse block using arch of the foot).

U-2. Using the same leg in *Ashigatana* position (footsword), he kicks the opponent's throat.

U-3. Or, after blocking the thrust with *Soko-ashi* (arch of the foot) he can then kick the opponent's face using the same leg in *Ashigatana* position (footsword).

U — 2

U — 1

U — 3

A

JIYU-KUMITE
(FREE SPARRING)

B

Free sparring is the pinnacle of karate. Until you have mastered free sparring, you cannot consider yourself to have learned true karate, but merely a form of gymnastics.

It is of the utmost importance for the karateka to develop swift reflexes and the ability to respond instantly to an opponent's moves. A good exercise to increase speed while changing directions is to place five chairs within a square area in the design of the number 5 side of a die. Then run around each chair as fast as possible within one minute. Another good exercise is to perform jump kicks from a squat position as many times as possible.

A. Two participants performing *Yoko-tobi-geri* (side jump kick).

B. The moment when an attacker is at the pinnacle of his jump.

C. One performs *Yoko-geri* (side kick) and the other *Mawashi-geri* (roundhouse kick).

D. At the same time one blocks an opponent's attack, he grabs the opponent by the collar and jumps up in the air.

E. At the same time one blocks the opponent's attack, he pulls the opponent down by the collar and proceeds to attack him using his right fist.

K. One child performing *Mawashi-geri* (roundhouse kick) and the other *Yoko-geri* (side kick).

L. One child is blocking the opponent's *Mawashi-geri* (roundhouse kick) with his arm and at the same time attacks the opponent's face with a front kick.

F. One performing *Mae-geri* (front kick) and the other *Mawashi-geri* (roundhouse kick).

G. At the same time one blocks the opponent's attack, he grabs the opponent by the collar and makes him fall. Then he strikes the opponent with *Migi-tegatana* (right handsword).

H. One performs *Yoko-tobi-geri* (side jump kick) and the other *Mawashi-geri* (roundhouse kick). Notice that the participants are wearing the new improved *Gi* or traditional karate garb (see page 238).

I. One performs *Seashi-geri* (instep kick).

J. A young boy performs *Yoko-tobi-geri* (side jump kick).

5. Tameshiwari

第六章　試し割り

Tameshiwari, the art of breaking wood, tile, bricks, and stone with the fist or the bare foot, is not a purpose of karate, but rather serves as a barometer of acquired strength and technique. It is useful for this purpose because in *Kumite* (sparring) you must never actually touch the opponent for fear of causing extreme physical injury. *Tameshiwari* allows the karateka to expend total effort and energy on an inanimate object, and successful results are indicative of one who has mastered his art.

Tameshiwari requires exceptional balance, form, concentration of spirit, and calmness. It is a challenge to the ability of the karateka and will test the limits of his strength. He must use all the power he possesses in order to succeed at each attempt.

THE DYNAMICS OF TAMESHIWARI

1. Materials used

A wooden board will always fracture along its grain. Therefore, the shorter the length of the wood grain, the easier it is to break. On the other hand, tiles, bricks, and cinder blocks are all synthetically manufactured and are therefore more homogeneous and lack lines of weakness. Due to this fact, these materials generally present a greater challenge to the karateka.

Probably the most difficult material for use in *Tameshiwari* is natural rock. The denser and more compact the rock, the more difficult it will be to break. (In general, the darker-colored rocks are the ones to avoid.) The beginner should only attempt to break rocks that are long and thin and exhibit planes of weakness.

2. Body contact areas

It is of primary importance that the striking portion of the body be as small and sharp as possible. This provides the object with the least amount of surface area to resist. Obviously when we say that the striking portion of the body must be small, we do not refer strictly to size as we would be unable to break hard objects with our little finger which is weak. Therefore, the striking part must be strong and powerful.

Obviously, human flesh and bone can never be as strong as rock or concrete and this is where technique and spiritual preparation enter the picture.

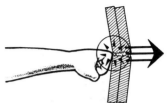

Weight x speed (high) > weight x speed (low)

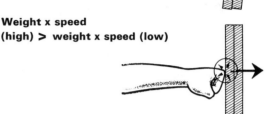

3. Power and striking angle

The strength necessary for the successful performance of *Tameshiwari* is achieved by marshalling all of the body reserves. Especially important is power generated up through the legs.

There are two ways to increase your power when performing *Tameshiwari.* The first is to take advantage of acceleration due to gravity. To understand this, think of this example: if a man weighing 154 lb. (70 kg.) stands on one foot, the earth receives a force of 154 lb. (70 kg.). However, if he jumps up and then hits the earth with one foot, the force will be greater than 154 lb. (70 kg.) due to the acceleration caused by the gravitational pull. This force can be increased even further by bending and stretching the hips while in the air.

The second method for maximizing the power of a blow is to strike the object perpendicularly; in other words there should be an angle of 90° between the arm and the object. If the object is struck from any other angle, the force of the blow is spread over the surface of the object rather than pinpointed.

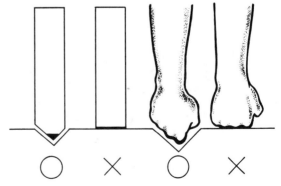

The sharper the striking point, the easier the object is to break.

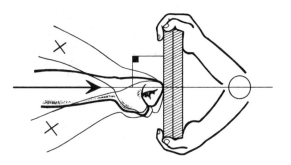

It is most efficient to strike the object perpendicularly.

4. Speed

The two most important things in *Tameshiwari* are power and speed. Speed is dependent upon many things including muscular strength, flexibility, bending and stretching of the hips, and quick reflexes. These can be acquired only through training.

Once the karateka has mastered all the spiritual and physical requirements, all that is left for him to do is constant practice.

5. Methods

As illustrated below, there are three possible methods for breaking an object. The first method, showing the object simply resting on two supports, is the most difficult and therefore least preferred. The next two methods are much superior. In both, a solid base such as the anvil pictured is used as support. One end of the object rests directly on the top of the palm which rests on a folded towel on the anvil. The difference between the two is in the positioning of the object. In one method, the end

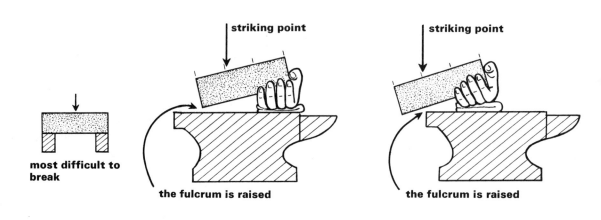

most difficult to break

striking point

the fulcrum is raised

striking point

the fulcrum is raised

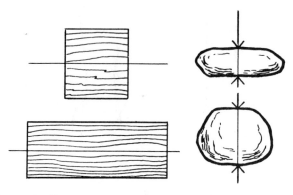

Theoretically, the top ones are easier to break than the bottom ones.

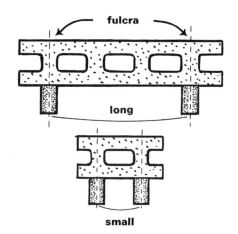

fulcra

long

small

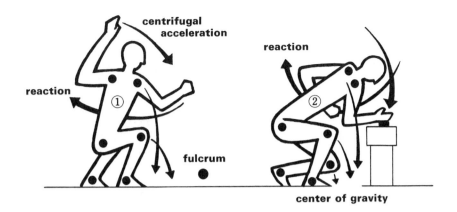

centrifugal acceleration

reaction

reaction

fulcrum

center of gravity

rests directly on the anvil, and you strike the object as shown by the arrow. In the other method, one-third of the object hangs over the edge of the anvil, and it is struck at the point shown by the arrow. In each case, before striking, the object is lifted by the supporting hand a finger's width off the anvil as shown. If you wish, you may cover the object completely with a towel or cloth in order to avoid injury to your hand. While it may appear that the last method is more difficult because you must strike the object directly above a support point, actually the sharp edge of the anvil aids in cracking the object.

Although the last two methods are very efficient for breaking one tile, they are not effective for breaking many tiles because of your inability to lift that much weight with one hand. The karateka must therefore use the first method which is more difficult because it lacks the additional breaking force acquired by the lifting of the object.

A — 1

A — 2

PRACTICING TAMESHIWARI

1. Tameshiwari using wood boards

Wood boards are widely used in *Tameshiwari*.

A-1. A boy breaking a wood board using *Tegatana* (handsword).

A-2. A 10-year-old girl breaking a wood board using *Tegatana* (handsword).

A — 3

A — 4

A-3. A 7-year-old boy breaking a wood board with his elbow.

A-4. A boy breaking two wood boards with his elbow.

A-5. Same as above, but with thicker wood boards.

A-6. Three wood boards being broken by *Seiken* (normal fist).

A — 5

A — 6

158

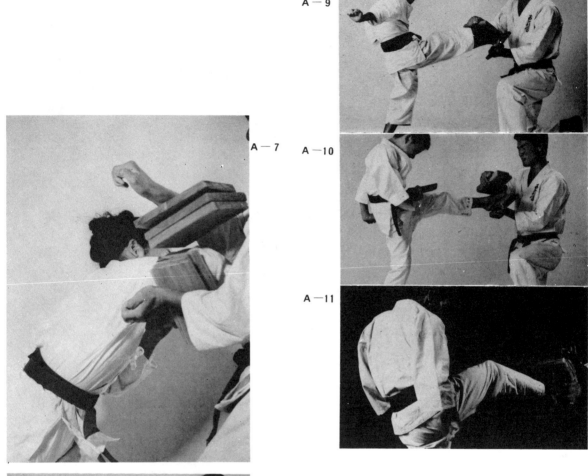

A-7. A woman breaking three wood boards using her elbow.

A-8. A 10-year-old boy breaking a wood board with *Seiken-tsuki* (thrust using normal fist).

A-9. A 9-year-old boy breaking a wood board with *Mae-geri* (front kick).

A-10. A boy breaking two wood boards with *Mae-geri* (front kick).

A-11. Three wood boards being broken by *Mae-geri* (front kick).

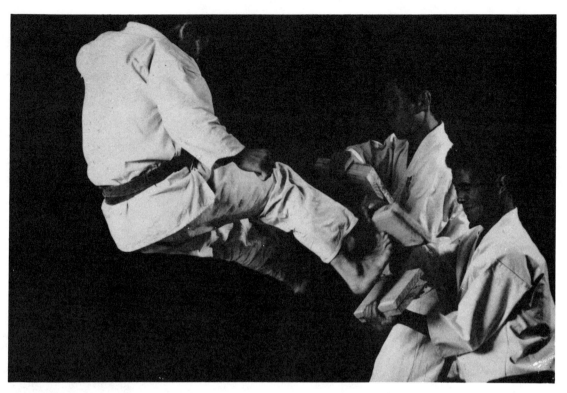

A—12

A-12. Four wood boards (two together at each side, as shown) being broken by *Ni-dan-geri* (foot attack from the air).

A-13. A man holds three wood boards.

A-14. The three wood boards being broken by *Mae-geri* (front kick).

A—13   A—14

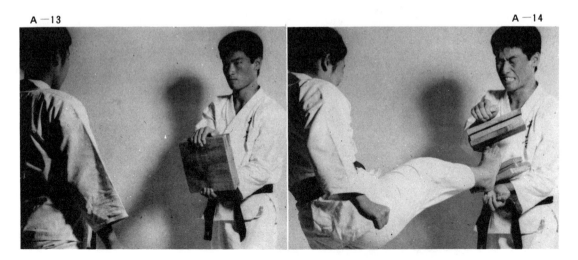

160

A — 1

2. Tameshiwari using tiles

A-1. Ten tiles are being broken by *Tegatana* (hand-sword).

A-2. Fifteen tiles are being broken by *Kakato* (heel).

A-3. Five tiles are broken by the head.

A — 2

A — 3

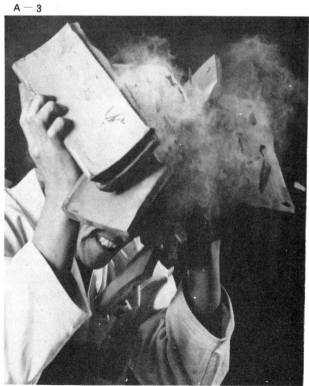

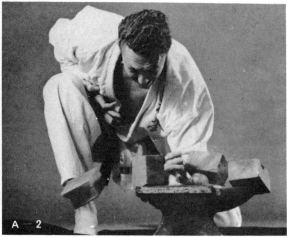

3. Tameshiwari using bricks

With a great deal of practice, you will be able to break two bricks.

A-1. One brick about to be broken by *Tegatana* (handsword).

A-2. One brick is being broken.

4. Tameshiwari using stones

A-1. A stone being broken by *Tegatana* (handsword).

5. Tameshiwari using cinder blocks

Cinder blocks are very often used because they have a homogeneous consistency.

A-1. A cinder block being broken by *Tegatana* (handsword).

A-2. A cinder block being broken by *Ashigatana* (footsword).

A-3. A cinder block being broken by *Maegeri* (front kick).

A-4. A cinder block being broken by the head.

A-5. A cinder block being broken by the elbow.

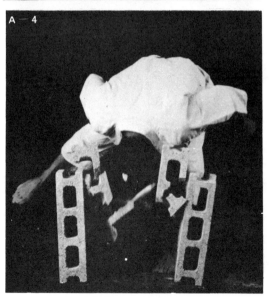

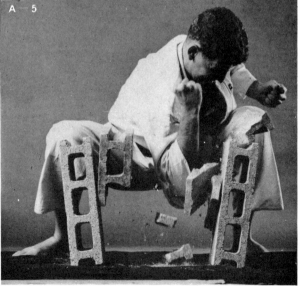

6. Special Applications of Karate Techniques

第七章
空手の
特殊応用

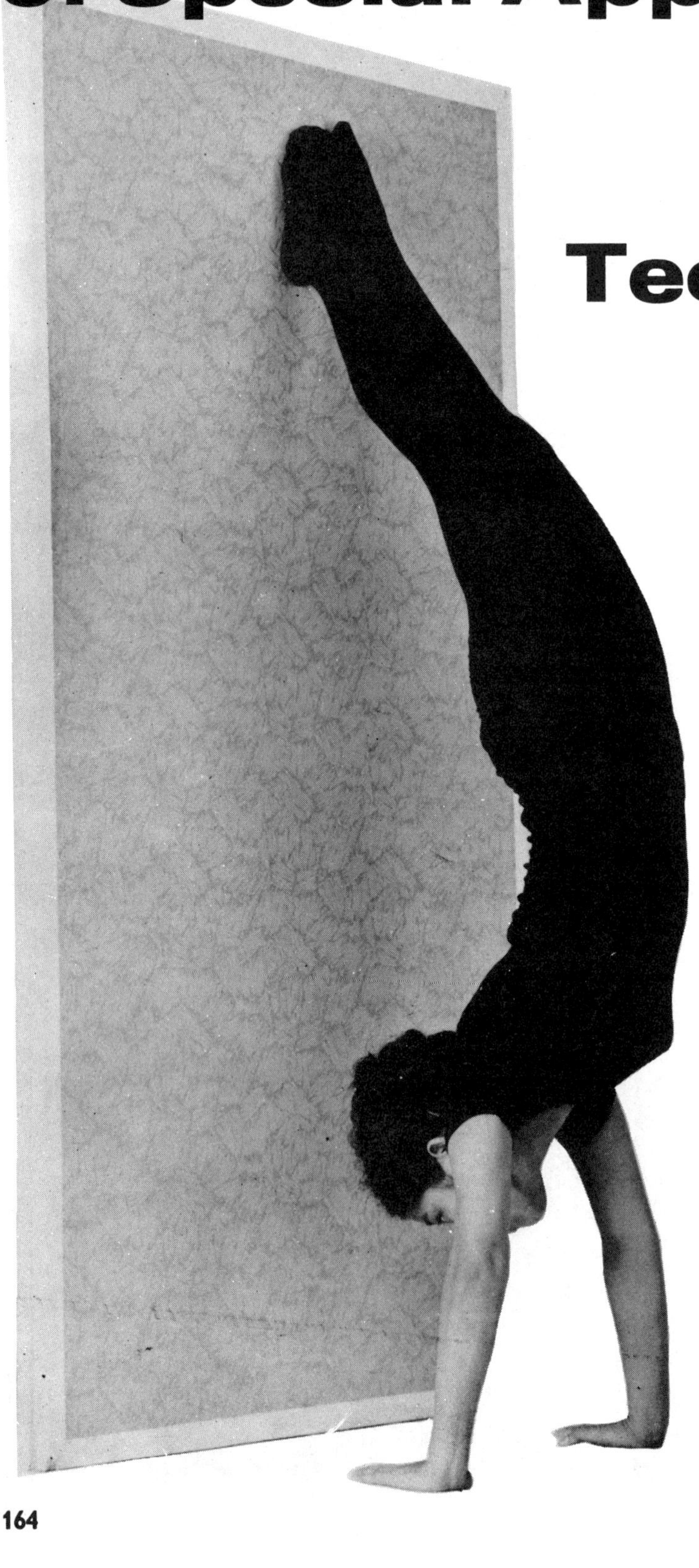

A — 1   A — 2   A — 3

Karate was first developed as a form of self-discipline and self-awareness, not as a sport. An ideal form of self-defense, it improves health, it improves the physique, it enhances spiritual and educational thought, and it provides a rhythm to daily life.

In this chapter, we shall examine the applications of karate that may be used in everyday life that recapture the essence of karate.

EVERYDAY TECHNIQUES FOR SELF-DEFENSE

Before describing the various techniques, a brief discussion on the importance of awareness is in order. You must have a *total awareness* of everything, no matter how trivial, that you do throughout your life. You must be alert to everything that goes on around you and not become lackadaisical. When your life is organized in this manner, it serves as a great stabilizing force and is psychologically and emotionally calming.

You will find the following techniques helpful in your everyday life.

1. While shaking hands . . .

A-1. When you meet someone, you shake hands with him.

A-2. If he steps in towards you with his right foot when you are about to withdraw your hand . . .

A-3. . . . and if he proceeds to throw a punch into your abdominal area, you can avoid it by following B. In B, a more careful handshake is shown. You must be aware that there could be an enemy even among your best friends, and be ever alert.

B-1. The handshake. Pay attention to the fact that you put your left foot in front, unlike in the handshake seen in A-1.

B-2. When you are about to withdraw your hand, he steps in towards you with his right foot as before.

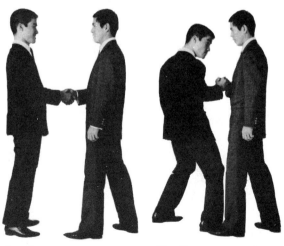

B — 1   B — 2

B — 3 B — 4

B-3. When he tries to hit your abdominal area with his elbow, you turn your body to the right and block his punch with your left arm.

B-4. As you block his punch, you immediately strike his face using *Migi-segatana* (right reverse handsword).

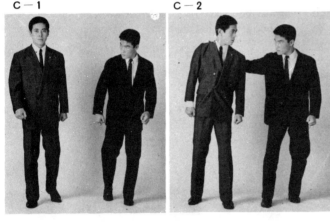

C — 1 C — 2

C — 3

2. While walking . . .

C-1. While you are walking, someone comes from behind to disturb you. You, then, move to his right side.

C-2. If he starts to grab your neck . . .

C-3. . . . you turn to the left using your left leg as a pivot, and strike him in his face using *Migi-segatana* (right reverse handsword).

D—1

D—2

D—3

E—1

E—2

E—3

E—4

D-1. Someone approaches your left side, immediately starts to provoke a fight . . .

D-2. . . . and then proceeds to grab your lapel.

D-3. As soon as he grabs your neck, you kick his testicles with the right knee (using the left foot as a pivot), and strike his jaw using *Migi-shotei* (right palm heel thrust).

E-1. If, while talking to him (facing him directly), he grabs your left wrist with his right hand . . .

E-2. . . . you raise your left arm to the side . . .

E-3. . . . and at the same time duck under his armpit and grab his wrist.

E-4. Keeping his wrist in your left hand, you move behind him, twisting his arm.

F — 1   F — 2

F — 3

F-1. While you are walking . . .

F-2. . . . someone beside you suddenly grabs your right lapel.

F-3. Stay calm and let him grab you. And then, quickly turn to him and strike his side using *Migi-segatana* (right reverse handsword).

G-1. While you are walking, someone suddenly grabs the right lapel of your jacket with his left hand.

G-2. You strike the elbow joint of his left arm using the right hand, and proceed to strike his face with your head.

G — 1   G — 2

H-1. Someone starts to bother you . . .

H-2. . . . and he seems to be determined to fight . . .

H-3. . . . and pushes your shoulder. In this case you can follow I in order to give you an advantage. This is an application of kinetics.

I-1. When he starts pushing your shoulder or chest, you first stand diagonally in front of him.

I-2. As soon as he pushes you, you push him back with your shoulder causing him to fall over backwards. In this way you can win the fight without violence.

J-1. If someone grabs your lapels with both hands, you should immediately suspect that he knows judo.

J-2. You step in and lower your hips, and then push his hands up forcefully using *Koken* (arc fist).

J-3. At the same time, bend down and grab his legs with both hands.

J-4. Pulling his legs towards you, try to make him fall backwards.

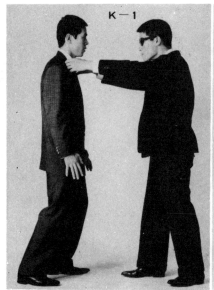

K — 3

K-1. Someone suddenly grabs your lapels with both hands.

K-2. Allowing him to keep a hold on your lapels, lower your body and open your arms outwards.

K-3. Using *Tegatana* (handsword), strike both his sides with your two hands.

L-1. Someone grabs your lapels with both hands.

L-2. You then throw both of his hands upwards using *Koken* (arc fist), and sweep them aside forcefully by hitting his wrists.

L-3. Immediately grab his neck and at the same time kick his testicles with the right knee.

L — 1

L — 2

L — 3

171

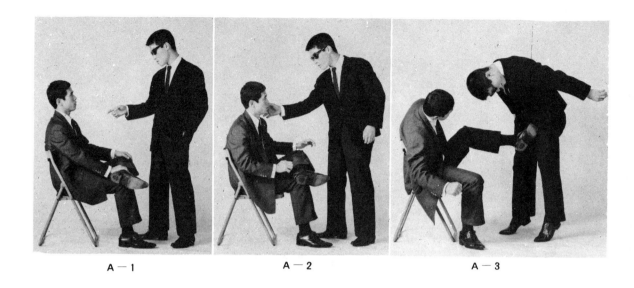

A — 1   A — 2   A — 3

3. While sitting . . .

A-1. Whenever you suspect some danger while sitting, you should always cross your legs.

A-2. If someone grabs for your neck . . .

A-3. . . . you kick him in his testicles using the upper part of the foot.

B-1. Suppose someone starts a fight with you when your legs are not crossed.

B-2. He proceeds to grab for your neck.

B-3. You immediately grab his right ankle with your right hand and pull it. At the same time, you push him in the stomach. This technique is very effective.

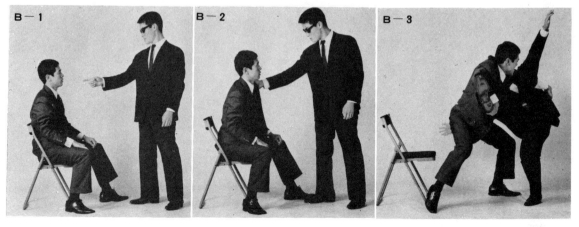

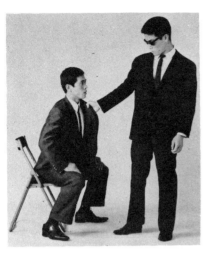

C — 1

C — 2

C-1. Someone suddenly grabs your lapel and pulls it.

C-2. You strike the joint of his right arm using *Migi-tegatana* (right handsword). You should stand up as you perform this act.

C-3. Then, you thrust at his eyes with the same striking hand. Or, you could strike his jaw using *Tegatana* (handsword).

D-1. When someone grabs your right lapel with the right hand . . .

D-2. . . . you can quickly stand up, and using your right hand make a hook over his hand. You then start to move to his outside.

D-3. As you move one step to his outside, at the same time grab his arm from the back and twist it while applying pressure to his shoulder with your left forearm.

C — 3

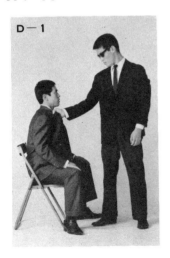

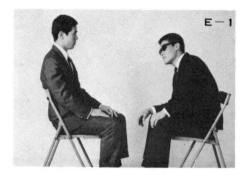

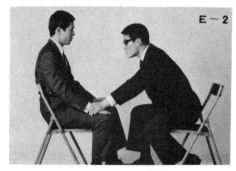

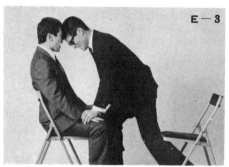

E-1. While you are sitting down and talking to someone . . .

E-2. . . . he suddenly grabs both your hands . . .

E-3. . . . and proceeds to butt you in the head.

This is a common attack and the following technique will help you avoid it.

F-1. You are sitting down, talking to someone, and . . .

F-2. . . . he suddenly grabs your two hands.

F-3. The instant you notice his head approaching you, quickly move your body to the side, avoiding his head strike.

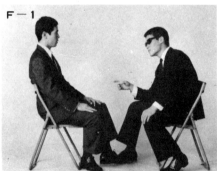

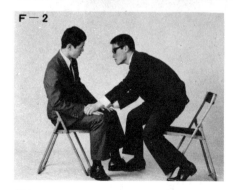

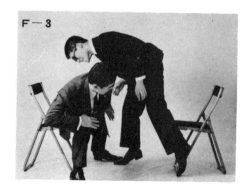

A－1

A－2

A－3

4. Self defense techniques for a woman walking

Nowadays, self-defense techniques are practiced among many women not only for self-defense purposes but also for the sake of physical fitness and beauty. Any technique must be practiced at least 100 times before it can be actually used as a self-defense means.

A-1. If someone suddenly grabs your left wrist . . .

A-2. . . . turn that arm outwards, and kick his shin with your left foot.

A-3. Then strike his eyes with your right hand. In this case, you should not put too much force into your blow.

B-1. As in A-1, if someone grabs your left wrist, step forward so that his hand touches your stomach.

B-2. Lower your left hand which has been grabbed and bend his hand back strongly.

B－1

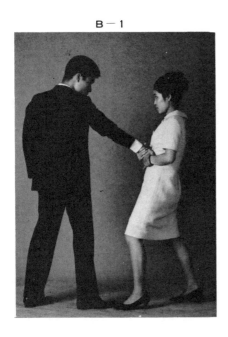

B－2

C — 1

C — 2

C — 3

C-1. If someone grabs your left wrist . . .

C-2. . . . turn your arm outwards and . . .

C-3. . . . hold onto his grabbing hand with your right hand.

C-4. Then grab his wrist with your left hand and bend it strongly. As he falls down to escape from the pain, kick him in the stomach.

D-1. When someone grabs both your wrists . . .

D-2. . . . open both your arms outwards to the sides.

D-3. Then step forward towards him, and strike his knee with your left knee.

C — 4

D — 1

D — 2

D — 3

176

D — 4

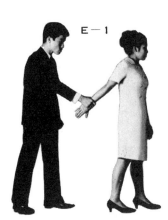

E — 1

D-4. Then kick his testicles with *Hiza-geri* (knee kick) with your right leg.

E-1. If someone grabs your right wrist from behind . . .

E-2. . . . turn around to the right to face him and hold his grabbing hand with your left hand.

E-3. You then bend his wrist the wrong way.

E-4. As he falls down, you kick him with your left leg.

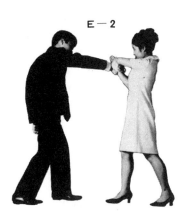

E — 2

E — 3

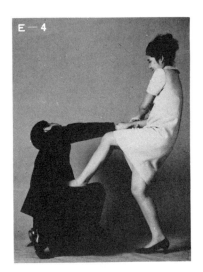

E — 4

A — 1

A — 1

A

A — 2

A — 2

5. Self-defense techniques using umbrellas

Everyone should be able to take advantage of whatever he or she is carrying at the time of danger, and this is especially true for women since they often carry handbags or umbrellas. Umbrellas are particularly effective in getting rid of muggers if you know the correct way to use them.

A. When someone grabs your left wrist . . .

A-1. . . . turn the left hand around.

A-2. Then step forward towards him and strike his jaw with your umbrella.

A -1. Or, turn your left arm around outwards (the arm which has been grabbed) . . .

A'-2. . . . and at the same time, thrust your umbrella into his abdominal area.

B-1. When someone grabs your neck . . .

B-2. . . . place the handle of your umbrella on top of his grabbing wrist.

B-3. Then, pull the umbrella down strongly using both hands. He will probably fall down to avoid the pain of his wrist being bent the wrong way.

C-1. If someone grabs your hand which is holding the umbrella . . .

C-2. . . . raise that hand upwards and place the handle of the umbrella on the back of his wrist.

C-3. Then grab the other end of the handle with your left hand, and step forward towards him in order to bend his wrist forcefully the wrong way.

B—1

B—2

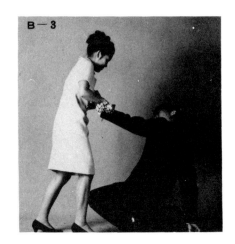

B—3

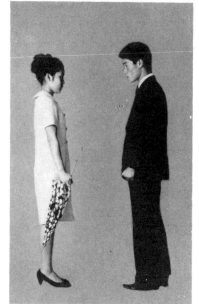

C

C—1

C—2

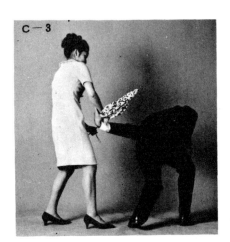

C—3

179

D — 1

D — 2

D-1. If someone tries to grab you from behind while you are walking . . .

D-2. . . . bend forward and lower your umbrella in front of you.

D-3. As you swing the umbrella downwards and back, bend over as far as you can in order to throw him over your shoulders.

D — 3

A — 1

6. Knife vs. karate

When someone threatens you with a knife, you should never panic. You should not retreat; instead, you must have the courage to defeat him even if you have to grab his knife.

To avoid panic when a real situation arises, you must practice the defense technique over and over with a partner. It is safest to use a rubber knife during practice.

A-1. Getting ready for the action.

A-2. Your partner strikes at you with a knife held in his right hand. You block him using *Hidari-shotei* (left palm heel thrust) from the outside.

A-3. As soon as you block, grab his right hand with the blocking hand. You then step forward with the right foot, and using that foot as a pivot, turn around. Then pull his arm over your shoulder using both hands and twist it.

A-4. While your left hand is twisting his arm, you attack him in the spleen area using the right elbow.

A — 2

A — 3

A — 4

181

B — 1

B — 2

B — 3

B-1. Starting from A-1 position, block the opponent's attack with *Migi-tegatana* (right handsword).

B-2. As you block, make a hook over his hand . . .

B-3. . . . and hold his hand with both your hands and raise it upwards while twisting it.

C-1. Starting from A-1 position, your partner lunges at your chest with both hands around the knife. You lower your body and avoid his attack.

C-2 and **C-3.** Then you kick him in the abdominal area using *Mawashi-geri* (roundhouse kick).

C — 1

C — 2

C — 3

D-1. Starting from A-1 position, your partner lunges at your stomach with a knife. You block it with *Tegatana-juji-uke* (X-block using handsword).

D-2. Then you turn his hand around and raise it, and at the same time bend his wrist and twist his arm.

D-3. With the right hand, you strike your partner's rib cage with *Tegatana* (handsword).

D — 1

D — 2

D — 3

E-1. Starting from A-1 position, your partner attacks you with *Jodan-tsuki* (upper body thrust). You block this by hitting his wrist with *Migi-tegatana* (right handsword).

E-2. Step forward with the right foot, and slide the blocking arm over his shoulder in order to get him in a headlock.

E-3. Put your right and left hands together and strangle him, and at the same time, pull his body over your right thigh.

A — 1

A — 2

A — 3

A — 4

7. Practicing everyday self-defense techniques wearing Gi (traditional karate costume)

Since self-defense techniques require a lot of practice, you must work on them every day at home, in a variety of real-life situations.

A-1. If someone attacks you suddenly in the neck . . .

A-2. . . . grab his attacking wrist with the right hand.

A-3. Then take his hand and turn around in order to twist his arm over your shoulder.

A-4. Lift your heels off the floor and pull down on his arm as hard as you can.

B-1. When someone grabs your right sleeve with his left hand . . .

B-2. . . . raise the arm which has been grabbed and turn it outwards.

B-3. Then grab his hand and lower it by putting your hand under his hand and grabbing his wrist with your left hand.

B-4. Bend his hand hard while raising his wrist upwards.

C — 1

C — 2

C — 3

C — 4

C-1. If someone tries to grab you from behind . . .

C-2. . . . take *Han-kiba-tachi* (half horse stance) position, and raise both your arms over your shoulders.

C-3. Then place the right foot one step back and strike the opponent in the solar plexus using the right elbow.

C-4. Now grab his left hand with both your hands and throw him over your shoulder.

D-1. If someone suddenly grabs your neck with his left hand . . .

D-2. . . . swiftly grab his wrist with your left hand. Then . . .

D — 1

D — 2

187

D — 3

D — 4

E — 1

D-3. . . . twist his wrist and proceed to place your right arm on his elbow joint.

D-4. By twisting his arm with your left hand and pushing his arm strongly downwards with your right arm, you throw him off balance.

E-1. When someone grabs your right hand, pull the grabbed hand in and quickly grab his wrist with the left hand.

E-2. Pull him towards you by his left hand, and move your right hand towards his right knee.

E-3. Hit him forcefully with your shoulder to make him fall down.

E — 2

E — 3

F—1

F—2

F—3

F—4

F-1. Same as E-1.

F-2. Turn your arm around, raising the fist upwards. This causes his wrist to become reversed.

F-3. Since this is painful to him, he will let his hand go. Immediately strike his jaw using *Uraken* (back fist).

F-4. Step forward with the left foot and kick him in the stomach with *Hidari-hiza-geri* (left knee kick).

FITNESS EXERCISES

An experiment was once performed on two dogs. One was deprived of sleep, the other was deprived of food. The dog that was deprived of sleep was the first to die. Proper sleeping habits do not only improve physical performance, they also relax the mind and allow it to operate at peak efficiency.

Importance of a proper diet

If possible, you should eat only naturally-grown fresh produce; avoid all foods that are artificially produced or loaded with chemicals. Eat with moderation and at carefully-spaced intervals. Try not to vary eating habits too much and never eat to excess. Make sure you eat lots of fresh fruits and vegetables.

Daily physical and mental health care

Today, when many of the physical diseases that affect us are caused by mental upset, it is of the utmost importance that attention be paid to the health of the mind. You must avoid circumstances that lead to excess tension or emotional pressures. For those situations that cannot be avoided, the discipline acquired through karate allows you to deal with adversity with a minimum of emotional upset.

1. Basic exercises

A-1. Stand straight in *Musubi-tachi* (open foot stance) position and place both your hands on your hips.

A-2. Now move your neck forward and backwards.

A-3. Then, move your neck sideways (left and right), and rotate it. You should do this routine at least 10 to 20 times a day.

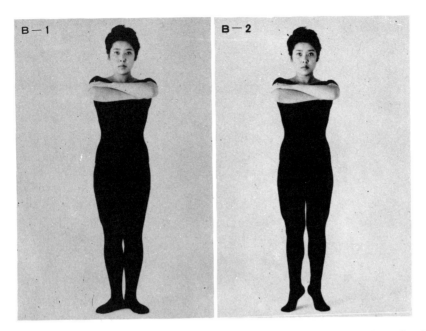

B-1. Stand in *Hida-ashi-tachi* (flat foot stance) with your arms crossed in front of your chest at shoulder level.

B-2. Lift your heels off the floor, so that you are standing on tiptoe. Then bring the heels down back to the floor, and repeat this about 10 times a day.

This exercise will strengthen the Achilles tendon and at the same time tighten the stomach muscles. It will also develop the gastrocnemius (calf muscle).

C-1. Stand in *Musubi-tachi* (open foot stance) position. Lift the heels off the floor and at the same time, raise both your arms to the side and bring them together over your head.

C-2. Lower your arms out to the sides. Keep them horizontal and bend your knees. Repeat this exercise at least 10 times a day. This exercise will tighten biceps, triceps, trapezius and deltoid muscles, and, at the same time it takes excess fat off your thighs.

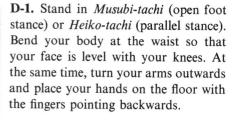

D-1. Stand in *Musubi-tachi* (open foot stance) or *Heiko-tachi* (parallel stance). Bend your body at the waist so that your face is level with your knees. At the same time, turn your arms outwards and place your hands on the floor with the fingers pointing backwards.

D-2. Then bring the body back to the original position, and without stopping there, continue on by stretching your upper body backwards so that the whole body is in an arc shape. Repeat this about 5 to 10 times a day. This exercise will strengthen your back muscles and also make your spine more flexible. It is especially recommended for those who have poor posture.

E-1. Start from *Heiko-tachi* (parallel stance) or *Fudo-tachi* (ready stance). Cross your arms in front of you so that your hands are next to your ears.

E-2. Then open your arms out to the sides in a large circular motion. This exercise will develop your pectoral muscles and should be repeated 5 to 10 times a day.

F-1. Stand in *Fudo-tachi* (ready stance) or *Heiko-tachi* (parallel stance). Bring the left hand up to the right ear. Do the same with the right hand, crossing it over the left arm.

F-2. Pull the right hand down to the right side of your body and at the same time stretch your left arm out in order to perform *Tegatana-naka-uke* (handsword block from the inside). This will tighten your arms and at the same time, it is a good exercise for *Tegatana-naka-uke*.

G-1. Stand in *Fudo-tachi* (ready stance) and then place your left foot forward to assume *Zenkutsu-tachi* (forward stance). At the same time, bring your right arm across the body so that the right hand is under the left armpit. Then bring your left arm over the right one towards the right side of your body.

G-2. Keeping this position, turn around 180°. In this way, you change from *Hidari-zenkutsu-tachi* (left forward stance) to *Migi-zenkutsu-tachi* (right forward stance). Now raise the right arm in front of you to perform *Segatana-uchi* (reverse handsword thrust), and bring the left hand down and behind the hips in order to perform *Shotei-uke* (palm heel block). This is not as difficult as it sounds. This exercise will sharpen your sense of motion, which is also important for self-defense purposes. Repeat this 5 to 10 times a day.

G-3 and **G-4** are the reverses of G-1 and G-2.

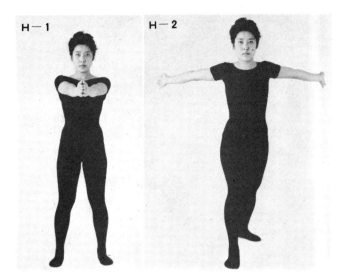

H-1. Stand in *Heiko-tachi* (parallel stance) position, and bring your hands together in front of you.

H-2. Then place the right foot one step forward and assume *Zenkutsu-tachi* (forward stance) position. At the same time, open your arms out to the sides in a large circular motion. Do the same in *Hidari-zenkutsu-tachi* (left forward stance) also.

I-1. From either *Fudo-tachi* (ready stance) or *Heiko-tachi* (parallel stance), bring both your hands in front of your body in *Koken* (arc fist).

I-2. Then open your arms to the side in *Shotei* (palm heel thrust). If you repeat this every day, it will develop the nervous system in your wrists and fingers.

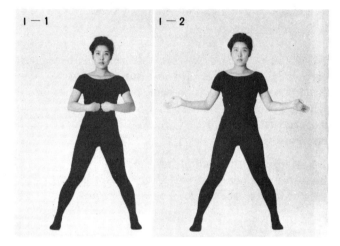

J-1. Place the right foot one step to the right side.

J-2. Bend the left knee and slide the right leg as far to the right as you can, keeping it straight. Repeat using the other leg. Alternate this exercise 5 to 10 times a day, and you will see a great improvement in control of your legs.

194

K—1   K—2

K-1. Stand in *Heiko-tachi* (parallel stance). Stretch the left arm straight to the left side, keeping the right hand on the right side at the level of the chest.

K-2. Then raise your right leg so that the middle part of the right foot touches the heel of the left hand. This exercise for hips and thighs should be repeated 5 to 10 times, alternating legs.

L-1. Stand in *Heiko-tachi* (parallel stance). Raise the left knee up so that it touches the left chest. This is a good exercise for knee kicks.

L-2. Repeat the same thing with the right leg.

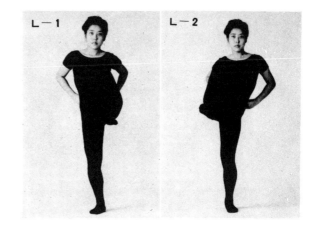

L—1   L—2

M—1

M—2

M-1. Stand in *Heiko-tachi* (parallel stance). Raise the right arm straight out and try to touch the right hand with the right foot, keeping the knee straight.

M-2. Do the same with the left leg and arm. This exercise will reduce excess fat around the hips. Do M-1 and M-2 around 10 times every day.

N-1. Stand in *Musubi-tachi* (open foot stance). Raise the right leg to the side without bending your knee. Then assume *Migi-yoko-geri-age* (right side rising kick).

N-2. Then bring the raised right leg to the front to assume *Mae-geri* (front kick). Since you do these two movements very quickly, you may find it difficult at first. However, if you look at it in terms of self-defense, it is very practical because you can strike two people at almost the same time. Repeat this exercise, alternating legs, 5 to 10 times every day.

N—1   N—2

O—1   O—2   O—3

O-1. Bring your left foot over to the inside of the right knee and hold your balance.

O-2. Using the left foot, kick to the lower left side as if performing *Kansetsu-geri* (kick to the knee).

O-3. With the same leg, kick backwards. This exercise is also a combination of two quick successive motions, as in N. Do this 5 to 10 times and repeat with the other leg.

P-1. This is a breathing exercise. Extend your arms out to the front, keeping the palms face down.

P-2. As you pull the arms up to the sides of your body, inhale. Then extend your arms out as in P-1, and exhale quietly.

P—1   P—2

196

Q—1

Q—2

Q—3

Q-1. Assume a push-up position. Then, stretch your arms out in an arc shape. Perform regular push-ups 5 to 6 times a day.

Q-2. Perform push-ups keeping your upper body bent.

Q-3. This is the front view of Q-2. This exercise will stretch your back. Q-1 and Q-2 should be practiced alternately every day.

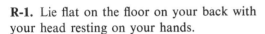

R—1

R-1. Lie flat on the floor on your back with your head resting on your hands.

R-2. Then clasp your hands behind your head, and raise your upper body off the floor. Continue to bend your upper body at the waist until your head touches your knees. You must keep your upper body stretched. Beginners should have someone hold their ankles, or hook their ankles at the bottom of a table or a desk. This exercise is the most useful of all for tightening the stomach muscles. It is also recommended for those who have weak internal organs.

R—2

197

S—1

S—2

T—1

T—2

S-1. Lie flat on the floor on your back.

S-2. Keeping your arms stretched flat along your body, raise the legs over your face so that your toes touch the floor far behind your head. This exercise should be repeated several times. It will improve blood circulation and also stretch the spine and the thigh muscles.

T-1. Sit on the floor with your legs stretched out. Then hold your ankles with both hands.

T-2. Bend your upper body so that your face touches your knees. This exercise will stretch the stomach muscles, quadriceps (thigh muscles), and gastrocnemius (calf muscles).

U-1. Sit on the floor with your legs spread apart.

U-2. Hold the right ankle with both hands and lean your upper body towards it so that your face touches your right knee. Do the same with the left leg. This exercise must be repeated 5 to 10 times on each leg every day.

V-1. Kneel forward on your knees allowing only the knees and the toes to touch the floor. Swing both arms

U—1

U—2

V — 2

to the back, and clasp your hands together and then bend the upper body forward.

V-2. Then, bend your upper body backwards so that your clasped hands touch your calves.

W-1. First lie flat on the floor on your back and hold your hips with your hands. Then raise the lower body off the floor starting with your feet, then hips and back, so that finally you are supporting yourself using only the upper part of the arms and shoulders. Stretch out your legs and start bending and stretching as if you were riding a bicycle. This exercise improves blood circulation and at the same time stimulates the working of the internal organs.

W-2. Lie on your side, and cross your arms in front of your chest. Bring your right knee up to the chest. Do the same on your other side using the left knee. This exercise should be done 10 times with each leg every day.

W-3. Sit on the floor and relax your legs. Then bring one leg up so that the foot rests on your head. Do the same with the other leg.

W-4. The handstand is a must in physical fitness exercises. At the beginning, you can try a three-pointed handstand, which includes your head as a support. In front of a wall, start by placing your hands on the floor at shoulder width. Then, kick your legs upwards until they touch the wall. Stay in this position for about 30 seconds. This exercise is perfect for improving blood circulation.

W — 1

W — 3

W — 2

2. Exercises using chairs

All the exercises here are ones which can be practiced almost anywhere whenever you have the time. It is best to do the exercises early in the morning when the air is freshest and you are not tired. Be sure to use chairs that have a wide base for safety, as shown here.

A-1. Stand by a chair and hold the back of the chair with your left hand.

A-2. Raise your right leg straight up to the side. In doing so, try not to bend the knee. Do not try to raise your leg too high at the beginning, but as you get used to this exercise, gradually raise the height of the leg.

B-1. This is the opposite of A-1. Stand by a chair and hold the back of a chair with your right hand.

B-2. Then raise your left leg straight up to the side. As you get used to doing this exercise, try to raise your foot higher than the level of your head. This exercise helps tighten the thigh muscles, and also helps firm the hips.

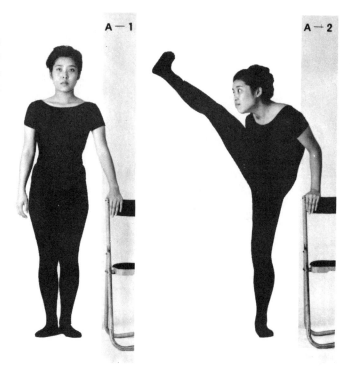

A—1   A—2

B—1   B—2

C-1. Place a chair on either side of you. Then, withdraw both feet one long step to the back and, holding the backs of the chairs with your hands, assume a push-up position.

C-2. Then perform push-ups, holding onto the chairs. For an average active woman, 1 to 3 times a day would be enough, although physically strong women may do this exercise 5 to 6 times a day. This will develop the muscles around the upper part of your arms and reduce excess fat.

D-1. Hold the backs of both chairs with your hands, and kneel on the floor.

D-2. Then push hard on your arms in order to lift your body off the floor using *only* your arms. This is quite a difficult exercise; however, if you practice it often, you will soon master it.

E-1. Hold the backs of both chairs with your hands and lower your body. Keeping your left leg in front, stretch your right leg out to the back.

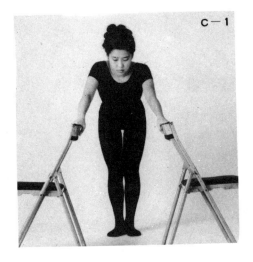

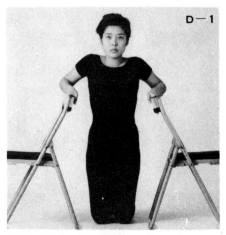

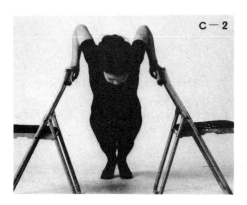

E-2. Repeat this, alternating legs. While doing this exercise, you must keep the upper body straight, and the stretched leg should never bend at the knee. This is beneficial for the back muscles, thighs, and lower body in general.

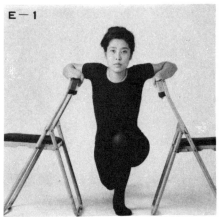

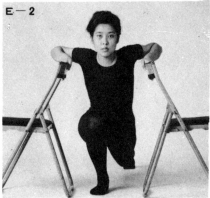

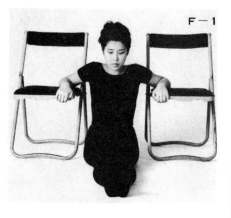

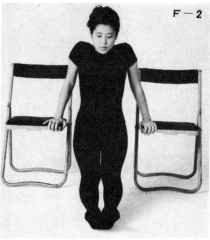

F-1. Place your arms on the seats of the chairs. Your hips are on the floor, and your legs are stretched out straight to the front.

F-2. Straighten your arms and lift your body off the floor. Then relax your arms and bring your body back to the original sitting position. This exercise is good for building the arm muscles, and at the same time, it straightens the spine. It is especially recommended for those with poor posture.

G-1. Holding the back of two chairs with your hands, bring the left foot to the back and place it on the right chair seat.

G-2. Then bring the left foot back to the floor and do the same with the right foot, using the other chair. Alternate this exercise several times. This is excellent for the ankles, knee joints, and hip joints. The twisting of the hips helps your internal organs develop and get stronger and also slims down the hips.

H-1. Sit on the chair keeping your back straight, and place your hands on the seat beside your hips.

H-2. Without bending your knees, try to bring your face down to your knees. This exercise should be done 4 to 5 times a day. It is good for the hips, spine, and stomach muscles.

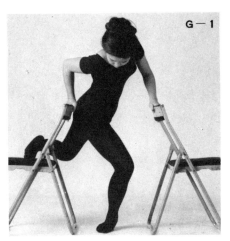

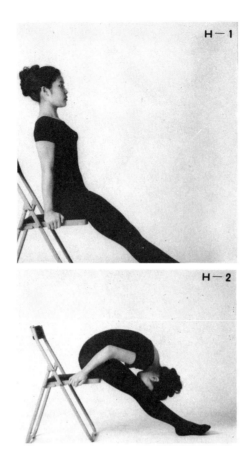

I-1. Sit on the chair and spread your legs wide apart and keep them stretched out straight.

I-2. Bring your upper body down, keeping the legs in the same position. The upper body should be bent all the way so that your head touches the floor. You should keep in mind that the spine must be kept straight while doing this exercise. This exercise should be practiced 4 to 5 times a day. It will straighten the spine and at the same time slim down the stomach area and strengthen the muscles there.

J-1. Sit back in the chair and hold the bottom of the back of the chair with both hands. Raise the left leg as high as possible without bending it at the knee.

J-2. Do the same with the right leg, and alternate this exercise several times. This exercise stretches the muscles of the stomach, hips, thighs, calves, ankles and the toes. While developing these muscles, it will also reduce extra fat around these areas.

K-1. Place both hands on the seat of the chair, and assume a push-up position keeping the arms straight. Using the right hand as a fulcrum, take the left arm away from the seat in order to make a large circular motion all the way to the left back. The body will twist around during this exercise. Then bring the left arm back onto the seat.

K-2. Do the same with the right arm, using the left hand as a fulcrum. This exercise promotes the development of the spine, hips, upper arm muscles, and also tightens the stomach area.

3. Exercises using a towel

Fitness exercises do not necessarily require special apparatus. On the contrary, you can practice various exercises using such an ordinary object as a towel. Since a towel is readily available and is convenient to carry around, you can do these exercises anywhere.

A-1. Stand in *Fudo-tachi* (ready stance) and hold a towel horizontally in front of you, keeping your arms stretched out straight. The width of your feet should be about the same width as your shoulders.

A-2. Keeping your arms and the towel stretched, bring the towel up all the way to the back of your neck. Then slowly bring it back to the original position, keeping the towel taut all the time.

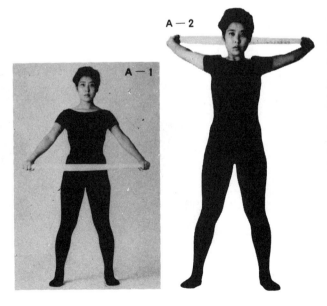

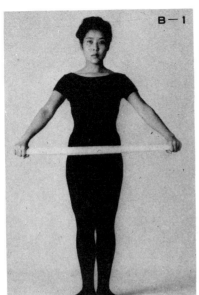

B-1. Stand straight with your heels together, and hold the towel horizontally in front of you, keeping your arms and the towel stretched out straight.

B-2. As you bring the towel up over your head, bend your knees and lower your hips. Then, as you get up, bring the towel down to the original position. This exercise should be repeated 5 to 6 times a day. This raising up of the arms will develop pectoral and deltoid muscles, which in the case of a woman, results in a firmer, fuller bust.

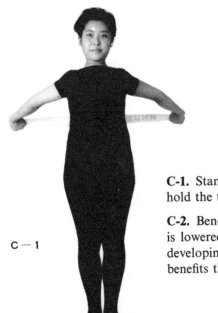
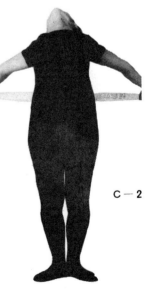

C-1. Stand in *Musubi-tachi* (open foot stance) and hold the towel horizontally behind your back.

C-2. Bend your body backwards so that the towel is lowered all the way down to hip level. Besides developing the chest muscles, this exercise also benefits the lungs.

205

D—1

D—2

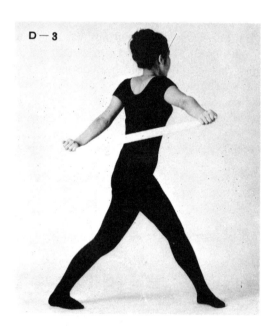

D—3

E—1

E—2

206

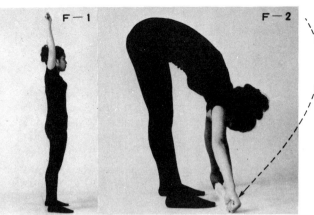

D-1. Stand with your legs apart and hold the towel horizontally behind your back, stretched out straight.

D-2. Turn your body to the right side, keeping the towel stretched in a straight line.

D-3. Now turn the body all the way to the left side. Alternate sides 4 to 5 times a day. This exercise will slim down the hips and will take away excess fat from around the mid-section.

E-1. Take the same position as in D-1.

E-2. Then bend the body sideways to the left side, so that the left hand touches the left foot.

E-3. This time, bend the body to the right side, so that the right hand touches the right foot. Remember to keep the towel stretched straight. This exercise slims down the stomach and hip areas, and should be practiced 4 to 5 times a day.

F-1. Stand up straight, and hold the towel horizontally above your head.

F-2. Bend the body slowly forward, keeping the towel taut, until the towel touches the floor right in front of your feet. This exercise will develop your abdominal muscles, and should be practiced 4 to 5 times a day.

G-1. Stand with your feet close together, and hold the towel behind your calves.

G-2. Bring the towel all the way up and above your head, and then down the other side until your face touches your knees. All this time, your arms must be kept straight. This exercise will develop pectoral and deltoid muscles, and should be practiced 4 to 5 times a day.

H—1

H—2

H-1. Stand in *Heiko-tachi* (parallel stance).

H-2. Lean back about 15°, and bring the towel up and above your head. Return to the original position. This exercise should be done 4 to 5 times a day. It will reduce excess fat in the stomach area and also develop the pectoral and deltoid muscles.

I-1. Stand in *Heisoku-tachi* (blocked foot stance) and bend the upper body forward, keeping the towel stretched straight behind your knees.

I-2. With the towel stretched, bring it all the way up to the back of your neck. This exercise is extremely good for slimming down the upper arms. It should be practiced 4 to 5 times a day.

I — 1

I — 2

SPECIAL TRAINING EXERCISES

A karateka must develop a strong body that can withstand any attacks. Although this cannot be done in one day, it is possible if you have enough will power to endure a long training regimen.

Having a strong body is not only necessary for karate, but it also enables you to respond quickly to any stimuli. Shown here are some important special training methods and their effects. You should always keep in mind that the techniques of karate can be acquired only when you have formed the basis for them: *a strong and flexible body*.

1. Exercises using *Makiwara* (karate striking board)

In past times, *Makiwara* was always hand-made of straw and rope wrapped around a wooden board. Today it is manufactured of sponge and steel springs. It does not matter which one you use so long as you hit it accurately. When you are using *Seiken* (normal fist) to strike the board, you should hit it with the knuckes of the first two fingers (see photo below).

First, assume *Zenkutsu-tachi* (forward stance). To begin, hit the board 10 to 15 times lightly and accurately until you get the feeling of it. Then hit

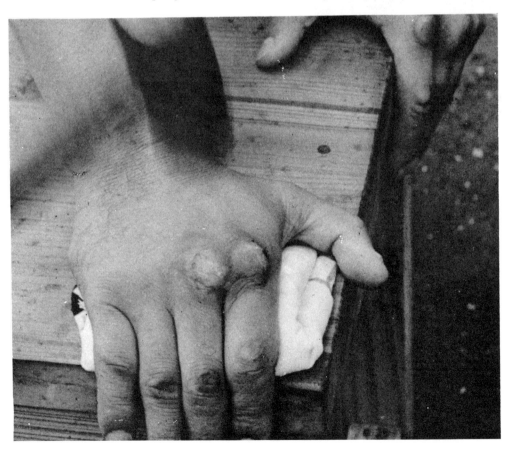

ease, without tension. However, the moment you hit the board, you should concentrate all your bodily power in the fist. Just before hitting the board, you should exhale, and as you withdraw your fist from the board you should inhale.

A-1. Preparing to perform *Migi-seiken-tsuki* (thrust using right normal fist).

A-2. The moment of impact with *Migi-seiken-tsuki*. The arm should be kept straight, and the body should be stable without trembling or shaking.

B-1. Getting ready to perform *Hidari-seiken-tsuki* (thrust with left normal fist).

B-2. The moment of impact with *Hidari-seiken-tsuki*.

C-1. Preparing for *Uraken-sayu-uchi* (back fist one-two punch).

C-2. The moment of impact with *Uraken-sayu-uchi*. You should practice this about 30 to 50 times a day, although this depends upon an individual's strength. Generally, in the beginning you must practice 10 to 20 times a day, gradually increasing as the hands become toughened. You must not practice so much that your skin breaks and starts bleeding. Do not overdo, but remember that if you practice regularly for a long time, your fists will become hard and strong naturally.

it more forcefully afterwards. You should hit it at least 50 times using each hand. Both hands should be exercised equally. While practicing in this manner, you should keep your body at

C—1   C—2

D. Take a preparatory stance for performing *Seiken-tsuki* (thrust using the normal fist), and then strike the board using *Migi-uraken* (right back fist).

E-1. Getting ready to perform *Tegatana-uchi* (handsword chop).

E-2. The moment of impact with *Tegatana-uchi*. One should take *Heiko-tachi* (parallel stance) for the best results.

F-1. Preparing to perform *Tegatana-naka-uchi* (handsword cross-body chop).

F-2. The moment of impact with *Tegatana-naka-uchi*. When practicing this, you should be either in *Heiko-tachi* (parallel stance) or *Kiba-tachi* (horse stance).

G-1. Exercise for *Mae-geri* (front kick) using *Makiwara*.

G-2. Exercise for *Migi-yoko-geri* (right side kick).

G-3. Exercise for *Hidari-yoko-geri* (left side kick). Each of these exercises should be practiced 20 to 30 times a day.

2. Exercises using the sandbag

You can use the same kind of sandbag or punching bag used for training boxers. It will help you increase the speed of your attacks, and strengthen the fists and the shoulders. There should be another person holding the bag while you practice.

Depending upon your individual strength, you should practice each of these exercises 20 to 30 times daily.

A-1. Exercise for *Tegatana-uchi* (handsword strike).

A-2. *Tegatana-uchi* (handsword strike).

B-1. Exercise for *Uraken-shomen-uchi* (back fist frontal punch).

B-2. *Uraken-sayu-uchi* (back fist one-two punch).

C-1. Exercise for *Jodan-tsuki* (upper body thrust).

C-2. *Hiji-uchi* (elbow thrust).

C-3. *Zu-tsuki* (head thrust).

D-1. Exercise for *Mae-geri* (front kick).

D-2. *Hiza-geri* (knee kick).

D-3. *Mawashi-geri* (roundhouse kick).

D-4. *Mawashi-seashi-geri* (roundhouse kick using the instep).

3. Exercises using baseball mitts

You need two people for performing exercises using mitts—one to hit the mitts and the other to wear them. The person wearing the mitts should move them around to various places so that the person hitting can practice quick responses to the changes in position. These exercises will increase your reaction speed to changes in the position of an opponent.

The person hitting the mitts can also use gloves, which will prepare him for *Kumite* (sparring) using gloves. However, the effects are the same whether you use gloves or not.

A-1. Performing *Migi-jodan-tsuki* (upper body thrust using the right hand) wearing gloves.

A-2. The same as above, but without gloves.

B. Practice exercises of *Mawashi-uchi* (round-house thrust) as shown, *Seiken-uchi* (thrust using normal fist), *Ago-uchi* (jaw strike) and *Shita-tsuki* (strike to the lower abdomen). The karateka here practicing *Mawashi-uchi* is wearing gloves.

C. The person wearing the mitts should cross his arms in front of his face so that the other person can practice *Tegatana-ganmen-uchi* (handsword face strike) using both hands consecutively.

D. *Koken-age-uchi* (upper thrust using arc fist).

E. Follow-through after *Seiken-ago-uchi* (jaw strike using normal fist).

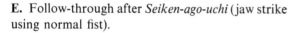

F. *Mae-geri* (front kick).

G. *Geri-age* (rising kick).

H. *Kinteki-seashi-geri* (kick to the testicles with the instep).

I. *Hiza-geri* (knee kick).

J-1. *Mawashi-seashi-geri* (roundhouse kick using the instep).

J-2. *Naka-ashi-mawashi-geri* (roundhouse kick using the ball of the foot).

K-1. Front view of *Yoko-geri* (side kick).

K-2. Back view of *Yoko-geri*.

L-1. Front view of *Yoko-geri-age* (rising side kick).

L-2. Back view of *Yoko-geri-age*.

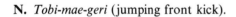

M. *Kansetsu-geri* (kick to the knee).

N. *Tobi-mae-geri* (jumping front kick).

O-1. *Tobi-yoko-geri* (jumping side kick).

O-2. *Tobi-yoko-geri* (back view).

P

P. Exercise for *Ni-dan-geri* (foot kick from the air).

4. Booshi-geri (kicking off a hat) and Tobacco-geri

When you have reached the point where you are confident that you can manipulate your body freely and can raise your legs as high as possible, then you are ready to practice *Booshi-geri* and *Tobacco-geri*. *Tobacco-geri* (kicking a cigarette from someone's mouth) is more difficult than *Booshi-geri*; however, it too, is only a matter of practice.

When you are able to use your feet and legs as freely and easily as you do your hands and arms, you are considered to be an expert.

A-1. Preparing to kick a hat off someone's head. At the beginning, you should just try to touch the brim of the hat rather than actually kicking it off. Once you get the feeling of barely touching the hat with your foot, then you should try doing it more forcefully so that the hat is knocked off.

A-2. The moment the hat is kicked off.

B—1

B—2

Examine the distance carefully before kicking.

C-2. The moment the cigarette is kicked out of the mouth.

B-1. With practice, a woman can do the *Booshi-geri* easily.

B-2. The moment the hat is kicked off.

C-1. *Tobacco-geri* must be done so quickly that the person smoking the cigarette does not notice it's gone. While practicing this, you should be very careful not to kick the other person's stomach, nose, or jaw.

C—1

C—2

218

5. Exercise using the Shishaku-bo (1.2-metre-long (4-foot-long) rod)

In karate, we use rods not to become expert at handling them as weapons but in order to acquire strength and good balance of the body.

A-1. Hold the *Shishaku-bo* horizontally in front of you.

A-2. Then, raise it back over your head and finally bring it back to the original position. This is an exercise for the upper body, especially the pectoral muscles.

B-1. Hold the *Shishaku-bo* upright at the right side of your body.

B-2. Using your left hand as a fulcrum, bring the rod downwards, making a large circular motion.

C-1. Do the same using the other arm. This exercise should be repeated about 20 times with each arm.

C-2. The position after the swing.

D-1. Bring the rod behind your back horizontally, and hold onto it with both hands.

D-2. Turn to the left as far as possible without moving your feet . . .

D-3. . . . and then turn to the right. This exercise will strengthen the hips.

E-1. Bring the rod straight down over your head and behind your back, holding it with both hands above your head. If the right hand is holding the end of the rod, then your left foot should be in front, and vice versa.

E-2. Keeping the same position, raise the rod and swing it downwards using a large circular motion.

E-3. When you swing the rod down, you must twist your wrists to make the movement easier.

E-4. Front view of a karateka swinging the rod downwards. Since the rod is very heavy, it will take a lot of training before you will be able to control the movement of it. At the beginning, you should practice using the rod slowly. Then, once you get used to it, increase your speed.

6. Exercises using barbells

There are three important things in karate: strength, speed, and technique. Out of these three, strength could be said to be the most important. However, strength is very much associated with speed; therefore, the karateka cannot achieve one without the other. From my experience, I can say that the karateka should devote himself to developing strength and speed while he is young, and not depend solely on technique. Karate techniques are expecially important for those whose physical strength may have lessened with age.

For developing strength, dumbbells and barbells are the best pieces of equipment to use. They are perfect for building muscles. However, too much strain on the muscles will result in slower speed. Therefore, you should not spend too much time in using these pieces of equipment. If you plan, for example, to practice karate for two hours a day,

20 minutes will be enough time to devote to body exercises using weights.

You should start with a barbell of the right weight for you or else you might injure yourself. It is best for you to learn how to use weights in a gymnasium under supervision. Never attempt *any* weightlifting without proper instruction.

A-1. Grab the barbell and bring it up to chest level. You should do this about 10 times.

A-2. As you get used to performing A-1, you should try to bring the barbell all the way up above your head.

B-1. Grab the barbell with your hands held in the opposite direction.

B-2. Bring it up above the head, and lower it to the back of the neck. This should be done 5 to 6 times.

C — 1

C — 2

C-1. Hold the barbell in the opposite manner again (the tops of the hands are facing the back).

C-2. Bring it up to the neck, and then lower it down to the original position. This is called a "curl." It should be repeated about 10 times.

C — 3

C-3. Do the curl with the hands held in the opposite manner.

C-4. Bring the barbell up to the neck. While doing so, you should not shake your hips or use a swinging motion to help you raise the weights.

C — 4

D-1. Grasp the barbell and . . .

D-2. . . . bring it up to the height where your arms are stretched straight down. Then lower it down to the floor. This exercise will strengthen the hip and stomach muscles.

E-1. Place the barbell on the back of your shoulders.

E-2. Then, keeping the barbell on the shoulders, bend the knees and lower the body. Then rise up to a standing position. This exercise will strengthen the hips and the legs.

F-1. Lift the barbell between your legs.

F-2. Holding the barbell almost perpendicular to the body, lower it close to the floor and back up to a standing position. Repeat this several times. This exercise will strengthen the legs, hips and the arms.

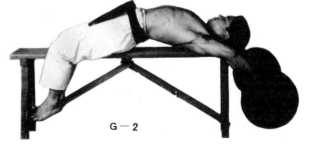

G-1. Lie on a bench on your back and hold the barbell up and above your face.

G-2. Then lower the barbell behind your head as far as possible.

H-1. This is usually called the "bench press."
Use a barbell of approximately your own weight,
and hold it right above your chest.

H-2. Push the barbell up until your arms are
straight, and then bring it down to the chest again.

226

I-1. Place both of your feet under the barbell, and hook them there. Clasp your hands behind your head.

I-2. Keeping your hands clasped, try to raise the upper body up over your knees. Then, bring your body back to the prone position. Repeat this several times. This exercise will strengthen your stomach and hips. At the same time, it will improve your internal organs.

227

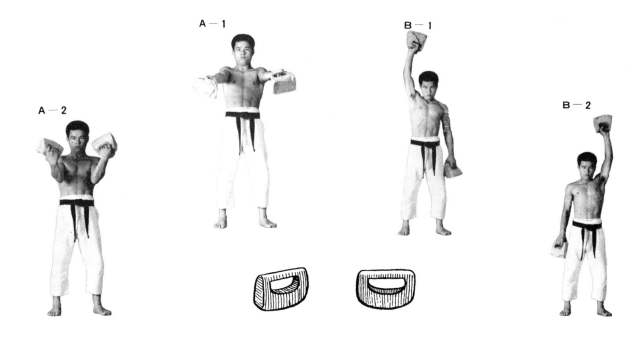

7. Exercises using Sashis (stone weights)

Sashis, stone weights with handles, have been used since ancient times in China, Korea, and Okinawa. Nowadays, however, it may be better to use dumbbells, which are the modern equivalent of *Sashis*. They are excellent for developing the back and side muscles, the wrists and your grip power. Here we show how to use *Sashis* for exercises, but if you prefer to use dumbbells, the techniques are exactly the same.

A-1. Hold two *Sashis*, one in each hand, with your arms stretched out forward.

A-2. Bend the arms all the way up at the elbows, and then return them back to the stretched position. Repeat this exercise about 10 times a day.

B-1. Hold two *Sashis*, one in each hand.

B-2. Raise one arm up above your head holding a *Sashi*, and keep the other arm beside your thigh. Then alternate arms. This exercise should be performed about 10 timcs each day.

C-1. Practice *Jodan-uke* (upper body block) using *Sashis*.

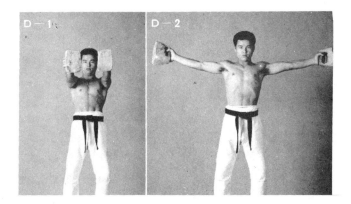

C-2. Practice *Hidari-jodan-uke* (left upper body block). This exercise will improve the speed of your arms, and should be performed about 10 times a day. It is more effective if you practice with light-weight *Sashis*.

D-1. Hold the *Sashis* with both hands stretched out forward.

D-2. Open the arms to the sides holding the

Sashis, and then bring them back to the original position. This exercise should be performed about 10 times a day.

E-1. Lie flat on the bench on your back, and hold the *Sashis* straight up.

E-2. Cross your arms in front of your chest.

E-3. Then, open up your arms to the sides.

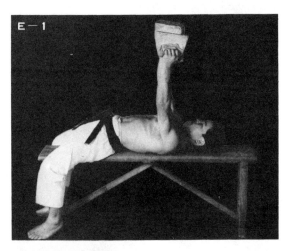

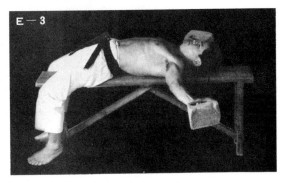

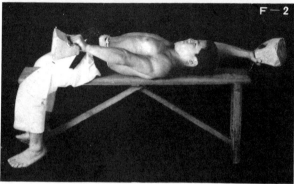

8. Exercises using Tetsugeta (iron sandals)

Tetsugeta were used by Japanese warriors in ancient times to develop strength in their feet and legs. They are still very popular since they can be worn on the hands or the feet during karate practice.

A-1. Hold the *Tetsugeta* in both hands.

A-2. Raise both hands with the *Tetsugeta* up and down in order to strengthen the pectoral muscles.

A-3. Then raise one hand at a time, and repeat with each hand several times.

F-1. Lie flat on the bench on your back.

F-2. Raise one arm holding a *Sashi* up above your head, while keeping the other arm beside your thigh. Then alternate arms. Repeat this exercise about 10 times a day.

A — 1

A — 2

A — 3

B-1. Hold the *Tetsugeta* horizontally in front of your chest with your arms bent at the elbow.

B-2. Open your arms sideways, and then bring them back to the original starting position. Repeat this exercise several times.

C. Wear the *Tetsugeta* on your feet and practice *Hiza-geri* (knee kick). When you kick, you should try to raise the knee so that it almost touches your chest. Alternate legs and practice about 10 times each day.

D-1. Wear the *Tetsugeta* on your feet . . .

D-2. . . . and practice *Mae-geri* (front kick). Be careful that the *Tetsugeta* do not fly off your feet! Alternate legs and practice this exercise about 10 times each day.

E-1. Wear *Tetsugeta* on your feet.

E-2. Practice *Yoko-geri-age* (rising side kick). You should always grip *Tetsugeta* tightly so that they do not come off your feet while practicing. This exercise should also be performed 10 times each day.

A

D

B

C

9. The bridge

As mentioned in the basic exercise section (pages 41–49), if you do exercises for the back muscles and stomach muscles, it automatically improves your internal organs and strengthens your hips.

A. First stand straight and then bend your body backwards.

B. Bend your body all the way down so that you can touch the floor with your hands, with your fingers pointed back towards your feet, thus forming a bridge between your feet and hands.

C. This time, keep your hands on your stomach and touch the floor with your forehead. This bridge should be rounder than the bridge in B. Since it will be a long time before you can do this bridge by yourself, you should use a wall to "crawl" down at the beginning.

D. Once you have practiced the bridge sufficiently, you will not move or shake, even if someone stands on your stomach. In addition, using your well-trained stomach as support, you can break tile, wood boards and bricks on it. Or, someone can

even break a stone with a hammer on your stomach.

E. Once you develop a strong stomach, you can withstand all kicks there.

10. Exercises for the handstand

Those who practice karate must do the handstand every day—even on those days when you do not do other exercises. The general public should also practice the handstand as a daily routine, because it will strengthen the internal organs and stretch the back and activate the respiratory organs.

A. In the beginning, you can have an assistant to hold your legs steady. You can also do this against the wall. You should spend at least 30 to 60 seconds a day doing the handstand, and prolong the time to 3 to 5 minutes as soon as you get accustomed to doing handstands.

A-1. Place both forearms on the floor and put the fists together, forming a triangle. Put the head right below the top of the triangle, and do a handstand.

A-2. The same as A-1, seen from the side. The headstand will help you develop balance before trying a handstand.

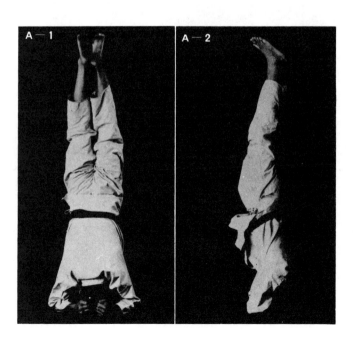

B-1. As you get used to doing handstands, try doing them with the fists instead of just the hands on the floor. Since the area the fists cover on the floor in order to control the center of gravity is much smaller, this type of handstand is quite difficult.

B-2. As seen from the back.

B-3. As seen from the side.

C-1. Eventually, you can try doing handstands with just the fingers. This handstand requires a lot of strength in your fingers; however, it is not so difficult to control your center of gravity since you are still occupying almost the same amount of space on the floor as with your full hand.

C-2. As seen from the side.

235

D — 1

D — 2

D-1. After you master the handstand with five fingers, then try doing it with three fingers, and even two fingers on each hand.

D-2. Standing on the thumb and forefinger as seen from the back.

D-3. Another view from the back.

D-4. As seen from the side.

D — 3

D — 4

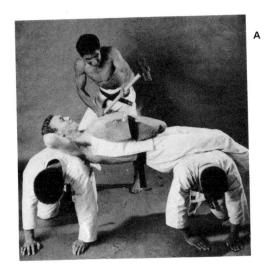

A

B

11. The mysterious and amazing body

After you have practiced all the basic exercises regularly for quite a long time, your body may be ready for some more training to increase its strength against exterior shock even further. After these exercises, the body becomes like steel.

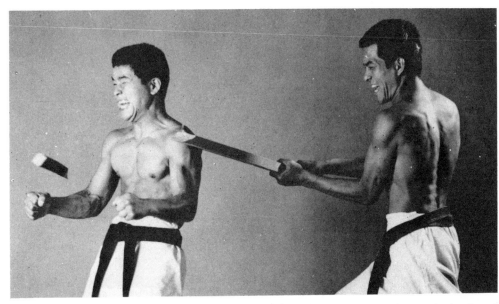

C

D

A. Lie flat resting the shoulders and thighs on the backs of two assistants. Then have a stone placed on your abdominal area. Another assistant breaks the stone using a sledgehammer, but your body should be hard enough to remain steady and without any damage to it.

B. Next, have an assistant hit your stomach with a 3- to 4-inch-wide (8- to 10-cm.-wide) wooden board. The wooden board will break on the hard abdominal muscles.

C. Have the assistant do the same thing to the shoulder muscles.

D. Have your assistant hit your trapezius muscle as hard as he can. Again, the wooden board will break.

237

12. Tumbling

It will take long and constant practice before you can do tumbling perfectly. In the beginning, you should have assistants holding a rope or standing by on both sides so that you can hold their hands as you practice. If you practice tumbling as an extension of somersaults, handstands, and flips, it will accelerate your progress. However, it takes about two years before a person with a well devel-

oped physical sense can master this perfectly, and for those who are not so well-endowed physically, it may take seven to eight years of constant practice.

Tumbling will sharpen your sense of balance no matter what situation you are in. You should be able to aim at any object or any opponent accurately and quickly however your body may be situated.

7. The New Karate: Modernizing Shiai (Competition Karate)

第八章

If you were to look carefully at all the different disciplines of karate that are being taught today, you would see that, ideally, there should be only one all-encompassing karate school. All of the practice methods, performance techniques, and forms of combat are essentially the same. The only reason to account for the fact that there are so many different schools of this sport today is that there are no general or comparative rules for the judging of competitions among the different schools.

In the modern karate contests of today, the competitors are never allowed to actually strike each other for fear of causing serious injuries. Therefore, contestants must halt kicks, punches, and other blows split seconds before making contact with their opponents. Because of this, it is not only difficult to judge the strength of an attacker's strike, but it is also impossible to predict accurately what effect the blow might have had upon the opponent if it had actually made contact with him. And, for the audience watching these watered-down contests, a large part of the excitement that would normally be generated in a contact sport such as karate is irretrievably lost. In addition, competition scoring is very difficult for the spectator to comprehend.

It is my belief that this type of match takes away a great deal from the very essence or spirit of karate. It is my proposition that competitors should be provided with protective clothing and other covering to make sure that all the vital areas of the body are protected. Then, the two combatants should be permitted to actually strike one another so that the judges *and* the audience can clearly see who is winning, and how the match is proceeding.

Karate should never be thought of or displayed as a vehicle for public entertainment. Nonetheless, so long as it is performed cleanly and according to the rules of the sport, interested spectators should be allowed to observe karate competitions. This would serve as an excellent way to promote and expand the general public's interest in the sport.

Of course, in order for our suggested plan for competition modernization to come about, the proper protective clothing and coverings are absolutely essential. Karate is a unique sport unlike any other, and it is therefore quite puzzling that the simple judo uniform, *Gi*, has continued to be used

A

B

C

D

TAMESHIWARI SCORING

Contestant	Seiken	Tegatana	Hiji-uchi	Mae-geri	Total Score	Rank
A	7	8	9	14	38	1
B	6	7	10	12	35	3
C	7	5	12	12	36	2
D	4	6	11	12	33	4
E	5	6	9	13	33	4

unchanged in karate for such a long time. Karate garb should be designed specifically for the rules and techniques of karate, the most important consideration being, of course, safety.

The photo on page 243 illustrates the essential parts of the modern karate competitor's uniform.

(1) top
(2) trousers
(3) abdominal band
(4) forearm guards
(5) athletic support
(6) shin guards
(7) belt
(8) gloves

Photographs A, B, C, and D illustrate how the new uniform is properly worn and how it looks from all angles.

Now that all competitors will be able to protect their vital areas by wearing the modern protective clothing, the contest rules should be changed to allow for physical contact. Combatants should be allowed to try to knock each other down using all the skills and techniques that they have acquired.

In modern karate competitions using the new protective clothing, matches should be broken down into four weight classes—lightweight, middleweight, heavyweight, and open weight.

In amateur competitions, the blows directed against the upper body of an opponent should be considered to be worth the highest points when scoring. The only exception to this would be a blow to the front of the face which should be considered a foul. The time limit for the performance of a karate match should be in the vicinity of 3 to 5 minutes. If, during this time period one of the fighters is knocked to the floor, he loses.

In professional karate competitions, the competitor may strike any portion of an opponent's body. The contest is terminated when one of the contestants is knocked to the floor. If neither combatant is knocked down within the set time limit of the match, then the winner is determined according to which man has recorded the highest score (in other words, the one who has thrown the most effective punches).

The group of professional karateka are the men who make their living through karate. They have accumulated much in the way of experience through years of hard training and continual practice. Because they perform in public competitions, they contribute beneficial and important services to the sport of karate in two ways. First, since they do not have to worry about getting into a second profession with which to support themselves, they can devote all of their time and energy to perfecting their karate techniques and methods. Second, they expand public interest in the sport by demonstrating karate to interested spectators.

In addition to karate competition involving *Kumite* (sparring) there is something else that must be given greater emphasis and that is the practice of *Tameshiwari* (the breaking of boards, tiles, stones, etc. by striking them with various parts of the body). *Tameshiwari*, when considered together with *Kumite*, should be taken as an accurate barometer of the strength that a karateka possesses. If one thinks of *Kumite* as a method for expressing the strength of a karateka's learned and applied techniques, then *Tameshiwari* may be considered a good method for judging his true physical strength. It is a mistake to look down upon the spectacular results of *Tameshiwari* as being overtly flamboyant or only "showing-off," or for that matter to practice it just for these purposes.

Currently, in *Tameshiwari* competitions wooden boards are used to measure a contestant's strength.

In the near future, however, we hope to be able to mass-produce a material with a more consistent make-up than wood. As is shown in the chart on page 245, there are four ways to measure the strength that is expressed when performing *Tameshiwari*. These are: *Seiken* (normal fist), *Tegatana* or *Shuto* (handsword), *Hiji-uchi* (elbow strike), and *Mae-geri* (front kick). Each individual score is then added together to determine the total score. In this case, Contestant A would be the winner of the over-all competition, although winners may be declared for each individual category as well. For example, Contestant C would be the winner in the *Hiji-uchi*, or elbow strike category.

In this way, if the strength expressed by each competitor when performing *Tameshiwari* would be compared to their performance of *Kumite*, one could make a fairly accurate judgment as to who really was the champion. We would consider any karateka who wins in both the *Jiyu-kumite* (free sparring) and *Tameshiwari* the perfect champion. However, it is doubtful, indeed, that there would ever be more than one perfect champion out of every 10 or 20 years.

Glossary

Japanese and English are very dissimilar languages and many words cannot be translated directly while maintaining their original meanings. For this reason, some Japanese words have more than one meaning in English and different words take on similar meanings. Therefore, the definitions of Japanese terms listed in this glossary and elsewhere in this book are offered as a general guide to the terminology of karate and should not be considered precise translations.

Age—rising, upper; a technique that starts low and finishes high

Age-uchi—rising strike

Ago-uchi—strike to the jaw

Ashi-barai—leg sweep

Ashigatana—footsword; the outer edge of the foot

Barai-oroshi—sweeping drop block

Birin—tail of dragon stance; preparatory technique for *Kumite* (sparring)

Booshi-geri—kicking off a hat, a practice exercise

Chudan—middle body; for example, *Chudan-tsuki*—thrust to the middle body

Enkei—in a circular motion

Enshin—center of the circle or pinwheel; a preparatory stance for *Kumite* (sparring)

Fudo-tachi—ready stance

Futa-ashi-tachi—two-legged stance

Ganmen—face

Gedan—lower body

Gedan-barai—lower body sweep

Gedan-tsuki—lower body thrust

Gendo-ma-ai—two steps (from your opponent); the maximum controllable distance between two participants engaged in *Kumite* (sparring) (see *Ma-ai*)

Geri—kick

Geri-age—rising kick, upper kick

Gi—traditional karate outfit

Gyaku—reverse, from the reverse position; using opposite hand and foot (see *Gyaku-tsuki*)

Gyaku-soto-uke—block from the outside from the reverse position

Gyaku-tsuki—reverse thrust; for example, left punch while stepping forward with the right foot, or while standing in *Migi-zenkutsu-tachi* (right forward stance)

Gyaku-uke—block from the reverse position

Han-heiko-tachi—half parallel stance; a stance similar to *Heiko-tachi* (parallel stance), but with the feet closer together

Han-kiba-tachi—half horse stance; a stance similar to *Kiba-tachi* (horse stance), but with the feet closer together

Heiken—flat fist

Heiko-naka-uke—parallel block from the inside

Heiko-tachi—parallel foot stance

Heiko-uke—parallel block

Heisoku-tachi—blocked foot stance

Hidari—left, using the left hand or foot

Hidari-zenkutsu-tachi—left forward stance; forward stance with the left foot forward

Hiji—elbow

Hiji-uchi—elbow strike or thrust

Hirate-tsukami—flat hand grasp

Hitosashiyubi-ippon-ken—forefinger fist

Hiza—knee

Hiza-geri—knee kick, kick with the knee

Hiza-geri-age—rising or upper knee kick

Hizo—spleen

Ibuki—a series of breathing techniques

Ippon-kumite—one form sparring; practice sparring technique in which a single attack is executed and countered

Ippon-nukite—one-finger piercing hand

Jiyu-kumite—free sparring

Jodan—upper body

Jodan-tsuki—upper body thrust

Juji-uke—X-block

Kaiten—turn

Kaiten-jun-tsuki—turn and thrust

Kakato—heel

Kakato-geri—heel kick

Kake—hook

Kake-ashi-tachi—hooked foot stance

Kake-uke—hook block

Kansetsu-geri—kick to the joint or knee

Kata—forms; a stylized series of practice moves performed against imaginary attackers in order to improve power, speed, and coordination

Keiko—chicken beak fist

Kiai—traditional Japanese term shouted when performing an attack

Kiba-tachi—horse stance

Kinteki—groin, testicles

Kinteki-geri—kick to the testicles

Koken—arc fist

Koken-shotei-uke—arc fist-palm heel block

Koken-uke—arc fist block

Koken-yoko-uke—arc fist block from the side

Kokutsu-tachi—back stance

Kote—forearm

Kumite—sparring

Ma-ai—a combination of the distance between you and your opponent and the speed of movement that each possesses

Maeba—the front part of the wing; a preparatory position for *Kumite* (sparring)

Mae-geri—front kick

Mae-geri-age—front upper kick

Makiwara—karate striking board

Mawashi—roundhouse; a technique using a turning or circular movement

Mawashi-geri—roundhouse kick

Mawashi-kake—roundhouse hook

Mawashi-seashi-geri—roundhouse kick with the instep

Mawashi-soko-ashi-uke—roundhouse block using the arch of the foot

Mawashi-uchi—roundhouse thrust

Mawashi-uke—roundhouse block

Migi—right, using the right hand or foot

Migi-zenkutsu-tachi—right forward stance; forward stance with the right foot forward

Moro-ashi-tachi—two foot stance

Morote—two-hand, using both hands

Morote-naka-uke—two-hand block from the inside

Musubi-tachi—linked foot or open foot stance

Naka—inner, from the inside; a technique that moves from the inside to the outside of the body

Naka-ashi—ball of the foot

Naka-hachiji-tachi—inner figure 8 stance

Naka-uke—block from the inside to the outside

Nakayubi-ippon-ken—middle-finger fist

Neko-ashi-tachi—cat stance

Ni-dan-geri—foot attack from the air

Nihon-ken—two-finger fist

Nihon-nukite—two-finger piercing hand

Nukite—piercing hand

Oi—lunge; a technique performed while moving towards the opponent

Oi-ashigatana—lunge footsword

Oi-geri—lunge kick

Oi-mae-geri—front lunge kick

Oi-mawashi-geri—roundhouse lunge kick

Oi-tsuki—lunge punch

Omote-ura-kake—front-back hook

Oroshi—drop punch or block; a technique coming down from above

Oyayubi-ippon-ken—thumb fist

Ryuhen—moving dragon stance; a preparatory technique for *Kumite* (sparring)

Ryutou-ken—dragon's head fist

Sage-uchi—drop punch

Sakotsu—collarbone

Sanbon-kumite—three form sparring; a sparring exercise in which three attacks are executed and blocked at the end of which the defender counter-attacks

Sansen-tachi—fighting stance

Sansen-tsuki—fighting blow

Sashi—stone weight

Seashi—instep

Seashi-geri—kick with the instep

Segatana—reverse handsword; a technique using the inner edge of the open hand with the palm either up or down

Segatana-uchi—reverse handsword thrust

Segatana-uke—reverse handsword block

Seiken—normal fist

Seiken-tsuki—thrust using the normal fist

Shiai—competition karate

Shiko-tachi—Sumo stance

Shishaku-bo—1.2-metre- (4-foot-) long rod

Shita—lower, from above; a technique that moves downward from above

Shita-tsuki—strike to the lower abdomen

Shotei—palm heel, palm heel thrust

Shotei-oroshi-uke—palm heel drop block

Shotei-oshi—palm heel thrust

Shotei-shita-uke—palm heel block from above

Shotei-sotogawa-uke—palm heel block from the outside

Shotei-ue-uke—palm heel block from below

Shotei-uke—palm heel block

Shotei-zuke—hip exercise

Shumoku-tachi or *Toboku-tachi*—T-shaped stance

Shuto—handsword (see Tegatana)

Soko-ashi—arch of the foot

Soko-ashi-uke—arch of the foot block

So-ou-ma-ai—one step (from your opponent); the closest you can get to your opponent during
   Kumite (sparring) and still maintain control (see *Ma-ai*)

Soto—outer, from the outside; a technique that moves from the outside towards the middle of the
   body

Soto-gedan-barai—lower body sweep from the outside

Soto-hachiji-tachi—outer figure 8 stance

Soto-uchi—outer thrust, thrust from the outside

Soto-uke—block from the outside to the inside

Tachi—stance

Tameshiwari—the art of using parts of the body, such as the hand, elbow, head, or foot to break
   wood, tile, bricks, stone, etc.

Tegatana—handsword or knifehand; a technique using the outer edge of the open hand

Tegatana-juji-uke—handsword X-block

Tegatana-kake—handsword hook

Tegatana-naka-uchi—handsword cross body chop (from the inside)

Tegatana-sakotsu-uchi—handsword collarbone chop

Tegatana-sakotsu-uchikomi—handsword collarbone punch

Tegatana-uchi—handsword chop

Tegatana-uke—handsword block

Tegatana-ura-kake-ue-tsuki—handsword back hook-upper punch

Tetsugeta—iron sandals

Tettsui—iron hammer fist

Tettsui-uchi—iron hammer fist strike

Tobacco-geri—kicking a cigarette from someone's mouth; a practice exercise

Tobi-ashigatana-geri—jumping kick using footsword

Toboku-tachi or *Shumoku-tachi*—T-shaped stance

Toho—sword peak hand

Tsuki—thrust, punch

Tsuru-ashi-tachi—crane stance

Uchi—thrust, strike

Ue—upper, from below; an upward moving technique

Uke—block

Ura—back

Uraken—back fist

Uraken-hizo-uchi—back fist to the spleen

Uraken-sayu-uchi—back fist one-two punch

Uraken-shomen-uchi—back fist frontal punch

Ushiro-geri—rear kick

Yoko-geri—side kick

Yoko-geri-age—rising side kick

Yoko-tobi-geri—side jump kick

Yoko-uke—block from the side
Yudo-ma-ai—one and a half steps (from your opponent) (see *Ma-ai*)
Zenkutsu—forward
Zenkutsu-hiji-uchi—forward elbow thrust
Zenkutsu-tachi—forward stance
Zu-tsuki—head thrust

Index